PERCY

HIS SONGS

by JAMES N. HEALY

Illustrations and
musical arrangements
by the Author

THE MERCIER PRESS
DUBLIN AND CORK

First Published 1966

Paperback edition 1974

Reprinted 1976
Reprinted 1977

ISBN 0 85342 394 6

Reproduced photo-litho and printed in the Republic
of Ireland by Cahill (1976) Limited, East Wall Road,
Dublin 3.

To the Misses Ettie and Joan French
who retain such a lively memory of their father
and to my beloved Aunts
who are all of
the same mind
and generation,
bless them.

PREFACE

PERCY FRENCH was probably the greatest, and certainly the most prolific, modern writer of comedy songs in the tradition of the Irish ballad. He had a regard for the people about whom he wrote which, apart from their genuine humour, gives his verses a special humanity and sets them apart from and above the ordinary comic song. "The Mountains of Mourne", "Come Back, Paddy Reilly", and even "Phil the Fluter's Ball", have a quality of wistfulness which makes one feel in sympathy with the absurdities of the characters as well as laughing at them.

A few years ago, when working on the production of "The Golden Years", I got the idea that it would be nice to have all Percy French's songs together in a volume for the first time, with notes on how he came to write them, and other such interesting facts about his quite unusual life as influenced by his writing, and when I mentioned this idea to his daughters I was glad to find that they liked the idea—so here we are.

This is not a biography, but an attempt has been made to explain him by giving a broad outline of his life as related to the songs, for the passage of forty years has dimmed the memory of this gentle man. He was seen in a different light by almost everyone who wrote of him after his death. He was, in his own way, something of an enigma. Alfred P. Graves remembered a haphazard, happy-go-lucky fellow drifting into the entertainment business by chance; his fellow-entertainer, Val Vousden gave a picture of a dreamy-eyed, forgetful, half-fey lover of children, while his cousin, R. B. D. French, saw that the aristocrat turned singer could, when needed, effectively snub an interloper. Collisson, his collaborator over many years, hinted at the practical entertainer and good companion who could often be surprising and sometimes exasperating, while French liked to present himself as having been a dunce at school and a slacker at college—a boy who never grew up, which indeed, to some extent, may be true.

"Friends and relatives often urge me to grow up and take an interest in politics, whiskey, race meetings, foreign securities, poor rates, options and other things men talk about . . . I am still the small boy messing about with a paintbox".

Certainly this singer, composer, author, versifier, engineer, painter, journalist, landowner's son had a varied career which is most interesting when viewed against the background of his time —the Victorian era—and of his country, Ireland, when both were beginning to feel the impact of tremendous social and political change. His life took a course, through all its haphazard career, which could hardly have been predicted, in an age of rigid social convention, at the time of his birth. Two things all writers agree on:—his great personal charm, and good feeling towards his fellow beings.

I have done my best to give the authentic versions of Percy French's songs from his remaining papers and other information available, but it must be remembered that he himself sometimes, over the years of performance, allowed occasional changes to slip in, or even deliberately altered a verse in order to bring it up to date. I have used the original, which is usually the published version, wherever possible.

I am grateful indeed to the Misses Ettie and Joan French not only for giving permission to use the words of all the songs but for putting up with me in conversation, correspondence and at their charming little cottage in Suffolk. I am also most obliged to publishers for their generous permission to use occasional extracts from the music (an entire list of music publishers is included at the end of the book), but in particular to Mr. Pat Howgill of the Keith Prowse Music Publishing Co., Ltd. Mr. Sam Denton of B.B.C. Northern Ireland has obliged with the words of several songs, and several other enthusiasts of Percy French, including Commander George Crosbie who remembered "Luke the Looney" from Clongowes days, and Mr. Vincent P. Shields of Loughrea who recollected the otherwise forgotten tune of "The Killyran Wrackers".

I hope all concerned will take this inadequate note as a means of thanking them. I myself have always had great pleasure in singing and listening to the songs, and hope that this book will pass in some way as gratitude to Percy French for having written them. Writing the book was a pleasure; I hope it gives pleasure to those who may read it.

James N. Healy
Lincoln Place, CORK.

1965

PREFACE TO PAPERBACK EDITION, 1974

Water has been flowing under more bridges than that at Finea, and in considerable quantities, since the day I started this book in 1962; its publication in 1966, and now. I have grown older (one of the difficult things in life being to grow younger), and many of the people who knew Percy French and helped me with the writing have faded away. Others have been in touch with me in various ways. Hubert Leslie sent me copies of amusing sketches he had made for a book of verses with Percy French which never saw the light. I got a letter which indicates that 'Paddy Reilly' went, not to America, but to Scotland; where he stayed for a long time before returning to Ballyjamesduff. His daughter, Mrs Quin, resided nearby; but apparently he was never heard to mention the song.

I was also advised by a train enthusiast that the engine in Ennis is 'Slieve Callen' and not 'Bessborough', and, moreover that the actual name of the engine involved in the breakdown was 'Lisdoonvarna'! I give these facts, like the character in Lewis Carroll, as they were told to me; not being an authority on trains. Also, there was, originally, a court case. The event of the train happened in 1897 — a Clare paper broke it to the world with the heading "Ass runs amok at Ennis Railway Station", and French took an action for 'loss of profits'. He was awarded £10, and the Company lost an appeal. In court he mentioned that he was writing a song about the event, and quoted some lines which do not, in fact, appear in the completed version. It was when the song came out in 1902 that the Railway Company contemplated the libel action, but, as mentioned on page 52, withdrew. They had enough, apparently, on the first occasion. For giving me the lead information on the above I am indebted to Mr. Patrick Taylor of Galway. I became happily acquainted with the present representatives of the Glynn family when on the Kilkee visit mentioned below, and saw the several delightful water-colours which French had given on his visits to them. Their uncle had been baronial director of the attached South Clare Railway rather than the West Clare, so his amusement must have been still greater.

In 1964 I was delighted to be asked to paint Percy French murals in Kilkee, where he spent such happy days. They are in the Marine Hotel, and it was one of those occasions. I got going at them one night after the bar had closed, and became so absorbed in the quietness that I worked the night through, going to bed like a zombie at 11.30 next morning. They had nearly been completed which was just as well, since there was a rather riotous party the next night, and everybody wanted to help. God knows what they might have turned out like, if they hadn't been safely varnished! Some time after, damp in the wall got at them, so I repeated them on raised boards a couple of years ago: being glad of the excuse for another visit to Kilkee.

I have come across other bits of 'Frenchiana' which, though of great interest to me, have no place in the present book; but all I heard seemed to add to the great affection people had for Percy French. That another edition of the book has been called for means that his songs continue to be popular, and one cannot but be glad for that. He has even survived an edition of "The Golden Years" which went on in London called "Phil the Fluter" which had about as much resemblance to Percy French as I have to the Beatles!

In January of 1970, to mark the 50th anniversary of his death, a plinth of Mayo granite was unveiled at his grave in Formby cemetary by Brendan O'Dowda, at a ceremony organised by the Liverpool Irish Centre.

Recently — at Christmas of 1972 — I was driving to Sligo to do a concert, and diverted from the main road to see the birthplace of Percy French (which is signposted) as it was just off the way. Clooneyquinn isn't even a reminding ruin anymore: it has been completely demolished, and a stone doesn't lie upon a stone. Time passes: so it goes.

James N. Healy 1974

CONTENTS

Music

Line drawings by James N. Healy unless otherwise stated.

Abdallah Bulbul Ameer

Oh the sons of the Prophet are hardy and grim and quite un-ac-cus-tom'd to fear But none were so reckless of life or of limb, as Ab-dal-lah Bul-bul A-meer ——

Sweet Marie

Moderate swing

I've a little racin' mare called Sweet Ma-rie And the temper of a bear has Sweet Ma-rie — I have back'd this mare to win and on her I've all me tin, So we'll take a trial spin, Sweet Ma-rie hold yet, hoult, Sweet Ma-rie, don't you bolt, Sweet Ma-rie shure you'll never win the Farmer's Cup for me Ev'ry daisy in the dell ought to know you mighty well for at ev-er-y one you fell, Sweet Ma-rie. ——

Phil the Fluther's Ball

with a gay swing

Have you heard of Phil the Fluther, of the town of Ballymuck? The

times were going hard with him, in fact the man was bruk, so he

sent an invitation to his neighbours one and all, as to

how he'd like their company that evenin' at a ball And

when writin' out he was careful to suggest to them, that

if they found a hat of his convenient to the door the

more they put in whenever he requested them the

CHORUS

bether would the music be for batherin' the floor with the

toot of the flute, and the twiddle of the fiddle — Ol

Hoppin' in the middle like a herrin' on a griddle — O.

Up, down, hands around, crossin' to the wall, oh!

hadn't we the gaiety at Phil the Fluthers Ball!

The Hoodoo

When de stars begin to peep and de moon am shinin' Into our cabin homes we creep Me and Lindy Loo, out of his cave dere comes de Hoodoo yes! dere comes de creepy, crawley Hoodoo, An' if a chile ain't in his bed De Hoodoo'll catch him sure

REFRAIN

Whisper low when twilight shades are falling Pull de clo'a-roun' de curly head To and fro I hear de Hoodoo callin' "Are dere any little pic-an-in-nies who am not in bed?"

Come Back, Paddy Reilly

The garden of Eden has vanish'd they say, but I know the lie of it still Just turn to the left at the Bridge of Finea And stop when half-way to Coole-hill — 'Tis there I will find it I Know sure e-nough, when fortune has come to me call — oh the grass it is green a-round Bal-ly-james-duff and the blue sky is over it all And tones that are tender, and tones that are gruff, are whis-per-ing o-ver the sea Come back Paddy Reilly to Bally-james-duff, come home Paddy Reilly to me —

Shlathery's Mounted Fut

briskly

You've heard of Julius Caesar, and the great Napoleon too — And how the Cork Mil-i-tia bate the Turks at Waterloo. But There's a page of glory that as yet remains uncut, And that's the war-like story of the Shlathery Mounted Foot! This gallant corps was organised by Slattery's eldest son — A noble minded poacher with a double-breasted gun And Many a head was opened, aye, and Many an eye was shut while Practisin' manoeuvres in the Shlatherys Mounted Fut And Down from the mountains came the squadrons and platoons Four and twenty fightin' men and a couple a' stout gossoons. An' whin we marched behind the dhrum to patriotic tunes. We felt that fame would gild the name of Shlathery's Light Dragoons

Eileen Oge

with a moderate swing

Eileen oge, an' that the darlin's name is through the Barony her
features they were famous. If we loved her who is there to blame us for
wasn't she the Pride of Petravore. But her beauty made us all so shy
Not a man could look her in the eye. Boys O boys! sure
that's the reason why we're in mournin' for the Pride of Petravore.

CHORUS

Eileen Oge! me heart is growin' grey Ever since the day you wandered far away
Eileen Oge! there's good fish in the say, But there's no one like the Pride of Petravore.

CHORUS OF Hannigan's Aunt

Then here's a health to Hanni-gan's Aunt, I'll tell you the reason why she
al-ways had things da-cent in the Hanni-gan family — A platter and can for
ev'ry man, what more did the qual-i-ty want? — "Ye'v yer
bite an' your sup, what's cockin' yis up!" says Mat-thew Hannigans Aunt

Maguire's Motor-Bike

It was Mick Maguire made it all alone and all unaided. For I tell you that a brainy boy was Mick, and for divilment and murdher, faith you needn't go no further than the bicycle he called the 'Kill-me-quick' oh the gearcase was a kettle made of good Brittania metal as good as you would buy in any shop, and when once you had it goin', Faith there never was no knowin' where ma-guires motor bicycle would stop but the bike's alright not a bit it mattered For the bike's all right and none the worse for wear. Oh! the bike's all right_ The rider might be shattered, but the bike's all right, so Maguire doesn't care

Mick's Hotel - CHORUS.

Oh yes, I've been there, Yes I was green there Hoping that the waiter might perhaps attend to me 'what's in that tur-een there?' "Soup sir, its been there" Never again for me!

"Are Ye Right There, Michael?"

You may talk of Columbus's sailing Across the Atlantical Sea — But he never tried to go railing From Ennis as far as Kilkee — You run for the train in the morning, The excursion train starting at eight- you're there when the clock gives the warnin', And there for an hour you'll wait - And As you're waiting in the train, you'll hear the guard sing this refrain— —"Are ye right there, Michael, are ye right? Do you think that we'll be there before night? Ye've been so long in startin', That ye, Couldn't say for sartin'- Still ye might now, Michael, so ye might!"

The Darlin' Girl from Clare - CHORUS.

And ev'ry man had got the finest plan, You ever see now Barrin' me now Every day there's one of them would say, That she'll agree now You'll see em all night they'd fight As to which o' them was right, in the colour of her eyes and hair. But not a word from me was ever heard about the darlin' girl from Clare

The Mountains of Mourne

Oh, mary this London's a wonderful sight, wid the people here workin' by day and by night: They don't sow potatoes, nor barley, nor wheat, but there's gang's o' them diggin' for gold in the street- At least, when I axed them that's what I was told. So I just took a hand at this diggin' for gold, But for all that I found it I might as well be Where the Mountains of Mourne sweep down to the sea

Fighting Maguire

Oh, Gibbon has told the story of old of the fall of the Roman Empire. And I would recall the rise and fall of a man by the name of Maguire. He came to our town as a man of renown, and peace was he said his desire, but we'll often relate what would be his sad fate, of the man who insulted Maguire

"Wait for a While now, Mary!"

I had plenty to do, and was only half through, and the bats were beginning to wheel when

who should pass by, on the road to Athy, but sweet little Mary O'Neill. Without

collar or coat, like a mountainy goat, I stood with my face going red; she had

bid me goodday, and was turning away, when all in a fluster I said :— "oh,

wait for a while now Mary, I've something more to say

wait for a while now Mary, you needn't run a-way! "it's

"oh, it's all very fine" says Mary "I can't stop here all day. Says

I "don't fret, 'tis early yet" That's all I found to say!

music of 'When Erin Wakes'

WITH SPIRIT

CHORUS OF 'McBreen's Heifer'

Now there's no denying Kitty was remarkably pretty, 'tho I couldn't say the same for Jane, But still there's not the differ of the price of a heifer, Between the pretty and the plain.

CHORUS OF 'Donegan's Daughter'

There were short men and long men, and weak men and strong men, and right men and wrong men were all to be seen: But Donegan's daughter from over the water, She gave them no quarter in Ballyloreen.

Little Bridget Flynn

I've a nice slated house, and a cow or two at grass; I've a plant garden running by the door; I've a shelter for the hens and a stable for the ass, and what does a man want more. I dunno, maybe So, And a bachelor is aisy and he's free, But I've lots to look after And I'm living all alone, And there's no one looking after me.

Bad Ballads for Baddish Babies

1) THE TACTFULLY PATERNAL

GAVOTTE TEMPO

"Little Bill he made an aeroplane, off to France he flew. But an udder Currant

caught him and our Bill is overdue! His Pa. from Dover telegraph'd to sho. at Campden

Hill – Don't worry dear! an over- draft just met our Little Bill.'

2) THE INFANTILE TYRANNICAL

Edwin and Angela are twins and, often kick each others shins But havn't

hurt each other yet - Their boots are made of flannel-ette They try to

lull each others hair, but Soon desist in sheer despair For hair is

very hard to lull when hands are cased in Berlin. Wool

3) THE ABSOLUTELY UNANSWERABLE

f Jocasta Jinks had one reply to everything and that was "why?" Her parents

were extremely keen in everything, except in children to be sure they had a dozen girls

and boys who wanted food and clothes and toys food and clothes clothes and toys

instantly

rit.

One day her father whispered "Come and see what Heav'n has sent to you and me.

fervently

Jocasta gazed with look intent upon the babe that Heav'n had sent

a tempo

and when Jocasta murmured "Why?" Her Pa and Ma made no reply

Bad Ballads d) The Frankly Homocidal

The parents of the Tompkins Kid were taught to do as they were bid and

as the Kid was fond of strife they led a somewhat harrass'd life. One day he order'd

them to die, they did so almost instantly. For in the rivers gentle breast they found a greatly

needed rest. one morning to the Kid's despair, he found them

Mr and Mrs Tompkins wrong side up with care with care

Jim Wheelahan's Automobeel

When Jim Whee-a-han made all his money in trade he said he'd as-

tonish the town. And he stuck to his word, as you'll say when you've

heard of the won-der-ful yoke he brought down 'twas the latest de-

-sign in the motor-car line, Parisien and very genteel a motor might

do for me or for you, but this was an auto-mo-beel —— Jim

CHORUS.

Wheelahans Au-to-mo-beel oh that was the Tath-er in wheel. He

telegraph'd down he would ride thro' the town next day in his auto-mo-beel

Flanagan's Flying Machine

'Twas Flan-a-gan found out the sec-ret of flight and made such a heifer of a

fair that Farman and Blériot, Latham and White Proclaim'd him the King of the

Air. And, mind you, I think he deserv'd his success For really he work'd very

hard. Six days out of seven his private address was the hospital ac-ci-dent

Ward! — But soon he was safe and serene And every day could be seen by

ad-miring crowds Loppin' over the clouds In his marvellous flying machine-His

marvellous flying machine

The Mary Ann McHugh — 1st part of tune

Come all ye lads who plough the seas and also seize the plough The

Cruise of a canal boat I am telling to ye now It was the Mary

Ann McHugh that braved the Angry Surf And bore away from

Mullingar with a terrible load of turf

All by the Baltic Say

oh once there was a Kaiser, whose head was of great size, sir; and lived, by telling lies, sir; All by the Baltic Say.

Cornelius Burke

when first I took up arms 'twas a faction fight in clare Re Burke's they were all there, and 'faik they did their share, my father said Cornelius, you've a mighty martial air, I think that you were cut out for a soldier. Then hur- -rah for the trumpets sound, But it don't fetch me around al- -lo, of course the battle don't alarm me, and hurrah for the bugle's bray that's my cue to stay away- I've taken an objection to the ar-my!

Pretendy Land

Oh, come little baby across the sea, come to Pretendy Land with me there's.

Jam for dinner and jam for tea, and sweeties come falling in showers When you

need not think before you speak But gabble and chatter and yell and shout where

lessons are only a minute a week and Playtime is hours and hours!

Over the blanket billow, over the sheets of sand,

When night comes down on Counterpane Town we sail to Pre-ten-dy

Land. Over the hills of Pillow By favouring breezes fanned with the

flag made fast to the bed-host mast we sail to Pretendy Land

CHORUS OF Drumcolliher

I suppose you've not been to Drum-coll-her?- Ye haih't, well now I declare You

wait till you've been to Drum-col-li-her. And seen the fine place we have there There's

only one street in Drum-col-li-her But then it's a glory to see — You may

talk till you're dumb, but give me old Drum. Drum is the place for me.

Music from "An Irish Girl"

(a) "Come all ye" (Page 151).

(b) "Girl on the Big Black Mare" (Page 158).

The girl that . . . . . etc.

(c) "THE HIGHWAYMAN" (Page 156).

When I was . . . . . etc.

(d) "HUNTING SONG" (1st Lines) (Page 153).

Oh, what is so . . . . . etc.

PERCY FRENCH AND HIS SONGS

"And tones that are tender, and tones that are gruff
Are whispering over the sea,
Come back, Paddy Reilly, to Ballyjamesduff
Come home, Paddy Reilly, to me . . ." . . .

MOST OF the songs of Percy French were written over half-a-century ago, but have recently enjoyed a renewal of popularity which has made the name of their creator a familiar one.

The man who wrote "The Mountains of Mourne", "Abdulla Bulbul Ameer" and "Come Back, Paddy Reilly" has been dead now for more than forty years so that personal memory of him is fading. The songs live today for their own charm, and no longer depend on their unique performance by the man who created them.

Percy French was a remarkable person: a member of the gentry who became a wandering professional troubadour, and who had all the artistic talents at his command—he was verse-maker and composer, artist and singer; story-teller par excellence. With only the songs to remember him by, it is perhaps forgotten, or not

realised, that he was one of the most popular entertainers of his
time with a solo performance which lasted over two hours, and
for which he wrote all his own material; an easy-going, amiable
man whose inner strength, nevertheless, enabled him to deal
calmly with a great amount of tribulation, and in his own surprising way, make a success of his life.

Many of the older generation will remember the little figure
with flowing white hair and moustache who came to entertain
them at Bundoran, Kilkee or others of the many seaside places,
for it was an event of his time when Percy French came to town
—whether the town was Dublin or London: Lisdoonvarna or
New York. They heard him maybe once or twice a year, and
then he was gone over the next horizon with his banjo, his bicycle
and box of coloured chalks; leaving them happy for the humming
of a new ballad, or with revived memories of one they had heard
before.

William Percy French was born on the 1st May, 1854 at the
family residence, Cloonyquin House, in the midlands of Ireland,
about ten miles from the town of Roscommon, and two miles
from the Tulsk Cross-roads on the Castlebar-Ballina road. His
father was Christopher French, a scholarly man who was a Doctor
of Law, and a Justice of the Peace. His mother came from Carrick-
on-Shannon, a town in pretty surroundings about twenty miles
to the north of Roscommon. She was the daughter of the Rev.
William Percy, who was the Protestant Rector of the town.

The French family settled in Galway in Elizabethan times,
and moved in the 17th century to Cloonyquin. There, they had
a fine estate, and so, for many years, were part of the "landlord"
class unpopular with the Irish peasantry because of the hard
application of the tenantry laws. This disaffection was the
cause of much trouble (as witness the affair of the notorious
Captain Boycott) but the Frenchs had a reputation as "good"
landlords, and the good relationship of the family with their
tenantry was the beginning of the love and understanding which
Percy French developed for the people of the land. By the time
of which we write, however, their fortune had dwindled so that
the second son of an impoverished landowner, third child
of nine, would have to make his own way in the world. It

was a time of rigid social convention, before two wars had the effect of greatly breaking down social barriers, and it was expected that he would follow a profession, and not make a living from "trade"; the idea of a member of a county family following a career on the stage just would not be thought of.

Cloonyquin has been demolished now for some years, a sign of the changing of the times in Ireland where the number of large estates are diminishing since they are no longer economic

to maintain; but Willie French (it wasn't until his professional days on the stage that he became known as Percy) had a happy boyhood around the countryside of his home in Roscommon.

From these days, wandering around the fields and misty bogs of that part of Ireland in which his youth was centred, he derived a love of the countryside and its people which expressed itself later on in delicate water paintings and his many songs. He loved animals; disliked people who were unkind to them; and in early years through the fashion of musical evenings spent in his own and in neighbours' houses, developed a talent for music and improvisation.

Early companions in life were the Godley family of Drominchin, from the neighbouring county of Leitrim, who shared this talent, and with the two brothers of the household he devised entertainments to amuse their own and surrounding family gatherings. He learned to play the banjo squatted over the fire of a country house in the winter evenings while Francis (later to become a Brigadier-

General) rattled the bones, and Arthur Godley banged the tambourine. On these occasions they made up songs and sketches related to small events in the doings of the family or people in the countryside around. This was the grounding for the talent of later years: Percy French learned the hard way, which is the most practical way.

During French's boyhood the family lived for a time out of Ireland, and Willie French commenced his schooldays by going to Prep. school at Kirk Langley, Derbyshire, and then, when 13, to Windermere College, also in England. It could not be said that at any time he showed any great inclination for killing himself with study, although owing to the possession of pleasant manners and natural ability time passed tranquilly enough.

The scholastic reputation of the second establishment—according to Alfred P. Graves, father of Robert Graves the Poet, who had been there before—was not high, but whether to bolster it up, or merely to please the parents, the headmaster, a gentleman named Puckle, was pleased to describe Willie to his father as "a genius at Maths." If somewhat taken aback by this statement the young genius hardly liked to contradict so eminent a person, and it lead his father to decide that he should become a member of the engineering profession, revising an earlier suggestion that he might follow his father into law, and possibly disappointing his mother who thought that the quiet, thinking boy might be destined for the church as his grandfather had been.

In order to prepare for engineering studies at Trinity College, he was sent to Foyle College for special coaching in Maths, and entered Trinity College in 1872. First of all, he worked for his B.A. and obtained it in the normal time in 1876; and then went on to complete the engineering degree which he finally took out in 1880.

At Trinity he quickly found occupations more congenial than study. As he said, "I think taking up the banjo, lawn tennis and water-colour painting, instead of chemistry, geology, and the theory of strains retarded my progress a good deal." He was a great success at College parties and concerts. For one of these concerts, in 1877, he produced an unpretentious ballad, the writing of which was eventually to lead him into a career far removed from engineering. Willie French, who might have lived, died, and been forgotten as a happy engineer, found the niche by which he would be remembered with affection when he wrote "Abdulla Bulbul Ameer".

ABDULLA BULBUL AMEER

As originally written

Written and Composed by Percy French. Original limited edition published privately by Percy French and Archie West.

Oh, the sons of the Prophet are hardy and grim
And quite unaccustomed to fear
But none were so reckless of life or of limb
As Abdulla Bulbul Ameer.
When they wanted a man to encourage the van
Or to harrass the foe in the rear
Or to take a redoubt they would always send out
For Abdulla Bulbul Ameer.

There are heroes in plenty, and well known to fame
In the ranks that were lead by the Czar,
But the bravest of all was a man by the name
Of Ivan Potschjinski Skidar*
He could imitate Toole, play Euchre and Pool

*Pronounced like a sneeze.

And perform on the Spanish guitar
In fact quite the cream of the Muscovite team
Was Ivan Potschjinski Skidar.

One morning the Russian had shouldered his gun
And assumed his most truculent sneer
And was walking down town when he happend to run
Into Abdulla Bulbul Ameer.
"Young Man" says Bulbul "Can your life be so dull
"That you're anxious to end your career?—
"For, infidel, know—you have trod on the toe
"Of Abdulla Bulbul Ameer".

"Take your ultimate look upon sunshine and brook,
Make your latest remarks on the war;
Which I mean to imply that you're going to die,
Mr. Count Cask-o-whisky Cigar."
Said the Russian "My friend, my remarks in the end
"Would avail you but little, I fear,
"For you'll never survive to repeat them alive
"Mr. Abdulla Bulbul Ameer."

Then the bold Mameluke drew his trusty chiboque
And shouted "Il Allah Akbar"
And being intent upon slaughter, he went
For Ivan Potschjinski Skidar.
But just as his knife had abstracted his life
(In fact he was shouting "Huzza!")
He felt himself struck by that subtle Calmuck,
Count Ivan Potschjinski Skidar.

The Consul drove up in his red-crested fly
To give the survivor a cheer,
He arrived just in time to exchange a goodbye
With Abdulla Bulbul Ameer.
And Skobeleff, Gourko and Gorschekoff too
Drove up on the Emperor's car
But all they could do was cry "och-whilliloo!"
With Ivan Potschjinski Skidar.

There's a grave where the waves of the Blue Danube roll,
And on it in characters clear
Is: "Stranger, remember to pray for the soul
Of Abdulla Bulbul Ameer."
A Muscovite maiden her vigil doth keep
By the light of the true lover's star
And the name that she murmers so sadly in sleep
Is Ivan Potschjinski Skidar.

Hailed with great enthusiasm by the students and their friends Abdulla was such a success that, with the financial assistance of a college friend named Archie West, French published a limited edition of the song. From this the two of them hoped to make a limited fortune: but he sold the rights for a five-pound note, and was ignorant of the necessity of registering his copyright, so a rude awakening was in store when they discovered that the song had been pirated by an unscrupulous London publisher, and a somewhat altered version printed with no mention of the author's name. This was before the copyright act of 1911 came into operation for the protection of authors, and so the unfortunate French had no recourse except to learn the bitter and early lesson that his song was being sold in hundreds with no profit to himself; for in a short time Abdulla was a popular song, in great demand at smoking-club concerts and similar assemblies. After the author's death a recording by the American singer Frank Crumit made the song so identified with that artist's name that in many places he was assumed to be the composer, and has been so described in several printed editions. The author himself gained nothing out of the song during his lifetime.

With the passage of time the firm who had pirated the song went out of existence, and were taken over by another establishment, who were themselves in time taken over. Through all these changes the song found its way to London publishers, who, we are happy to say, were good enough to make an arrangement about the copyright with French's family—up to then there had been no acknowledgement of the author at all. It was quite a source of annoyance to French during his life to see his carefully chosen words bowdlerised, particularly since it was the song

which set him on the road to fame; the changes were considerable,
as may be seen from one of the other versions when compared
with the original.

ABDUL ABULBUL AMEER

Later version of the original

The sons of the Prophet are brave men and bold
And quite unaccustomed to fear
But the bravest by far in the ranks of the Shah
Was Abdul Abulbul Ameer.
If you wanted a man to encourage the van
Or shout "attaboy" in the rear
Or storm a redoubt, you had only to shout
For Abdul Abulbul Ameer.

Now the heroes were many and well-known to fame
In the troops that were led by the Czar
But the bravest of these, whom no man could appease
Was Ivan Skivinsky Skivar.
He could imitate Irving, play Poker and Pool
And perform on the Spanish guitar.
In fact, quite the cream of the Muscovite team
Was Ivan Skivinsky Skivar.

One day this bold Russian shouldered his gun
And donned his most cynical sneer
Down town he did go, where he trod on the toe
Of Abdul Abulbul Ameer.
"Young Man" quote Abdul "Has your life grown so dull
That you wish to end your career ?—
Vile infidel, know you have trod on the toe
Of Abdul Abulbul Ameer".

Said Ivan: "My friend, your remarks in the end
Will avail you but little, I fear
For you'll never survive to repeat them alive,
Mr. Abdul Abulbul Ameer."
"Then take your last look on sunshine and brook
And send your regrets to the Czar—
By this, I imply, you are going to die,
Count Ivan Skivinsky Skivar."

Then the bold Mameluke drew his trusty skibouk
With a cry of "Allah Akbar"
And with deadly intent he ferociously went
For Ivan Skivinsky Skivar.
They fought through the night, in the pale yellow light
The din it was heard from afar
And huge multitudes came, so immense was the fame
Of Abdul and Ivan Skivar.

As Abdul's long knife was extracting the life
(In fact he was shouting "Huzza")
He felt himself struck by that wily Calmuck,
Count Ivan Skivinsky Skivar.
The Sultan drove by in his red-breasted fly
Expecting the victor to cheer
But he only drew nigh to hear the last sigh
Of Abdul Abulbul Ameer.

Czar Petrovitch, too, in his spectacles blue
Drove up in his new-crested car
He arrived just in time to exchange a last line
With Ivan Skivinsky Skivar.
A tombstone arose where the Blue Danube flows
And graved there in characters clear
Are: "Stranger, pass by, but contribute a sigh
For Abdul Abulbul Ameer".

A Muscovite maiden her lone vigil keeps
'Neath the light of the pale polar star,
And the name that she murmers, so oft as she weeps
Is Ivan Skivinsky Skivar.

French never approved of the changed version. In particular the double rhymes which he had been careful to build up in the penultimate line of each verse have been disregarded. "Toole" in the original was J. L. Toole, a celebrated comic actor of the time: "Irving" the tragedian was substituted for him.

French's Trinity days were happy ones. He had congenial companions: played a good game of tennis, (some of his happier topical satires are centred on the Fitzwilliam Club), and with his amiable character and talent for entertaining made many friends, but in Dublin French found his "Land of Heart's Desire" in a larger sense as he gradually became known to the musical, artistic, and theatrical circles. Symbolically enough the year of his arrival in Trinity coincided with the opening of the Gaiety Theatre, of which he was a frequent patron.

Two of his colleagues at Trinity, born in the same year as himself, were afterwards brought together in a brief moment of tragedy: but French would have had little in common either with the honest, though narrow mind of Edward, Lord Carson, or the brilliant but extravagent talent of Oscar Wilde.

After eight years he graduated. As he put it himself, "Eventually I was allowed to take out my C.E. degree. I believe the Board were afraid I should apply for a pension, if I stayed any longer in T.C.D."

One should beware of taking French's statements too seriously when he spoke about himself for his tongue was invariably in his cheek and he nearly always ran himself down. Take for instance his reply to the lady who, in later years in London, asked the exact spot from which he painted his "Sunset in Connemara". He volunteered to show it to her if she came up to 48 Springfield Road, N.W. Then there was the answer to a lady reporter's enquiry as to whether he had had any love affairs. "Love affairs? Why you seem to have forgotten my abduction of the beautiful Duchess of Gainsborough. Had to cut my way through a perfect forest of Ducal minions. You see this mark on my little finger? That was where one of the devils nearly got home. I was so altered by sword cuts and pistol shots that the lady did not recognize me and eventually married her former lover the Duke". In fact, considering that he took two degrees in the process, his career in Trinity was not delayed too much over the normal.

When student days were over French became an apprentice to Mr. George Price, Chief Engineer of the Midland Board. Mr. Price was blessed, not only with the priviledge of having the talented Mr. French, but also a friend from Trinity days, Charles Mansergh from Tipperary. They enlivened his days but neither stayed long with engineering. "I had two assistants," said Mr. Price in later years, "one danced and the other sang. One was Charles Manners, and the other was Percy French." In the following year Mansergh decided to make a living with his fine bass voice and changed his name to Charles Manners. In that year, 1882, he created the part of the Sentry in Gilbert and Sullivan's

"Iolanthe" at the Savoy, and later with his wife Madame Fanny Moody, formed the Moody-Manners Opera Company. In contrast to French he was a splendid business man, and his was one of the few touring opera companies to pay its way. One of their escapades, when with Mr. Price, was to appear together dressed as Christy Minstrels, for a joke, at Punchestown Races. It was their first professional appearance. They made 28/-, but tradition has it that their friends had the last laugh by making them walk home.

Charles Manners and Fanny Moody

Unlike most Irishmen, French had little interest in horse-racing itself although, apart from the amusing recitation "Carmody's Mare", he produced a couple of numbers racy with the fresh smell of the soil. He could ride a nag himself in his young days, and it is quite apparent that he at least knew all about country meetings—although his findings usually, indirectly, are that it is a mug's game—especially for those who put their money on.

SWEET MARIE

I'VE A LITTLE RACIN' MARE   SWEET

Music based on old American Tune

I've a little racin' mare called Sweet Marie,
And the temper of a bear has Sweet Marie.
But I've backed the mare to win, and on her I've all my tin,
So we'll take a trial spin, Sweet Marie.
    Hould your hoult, Sweet Marie.
    If you bolt, Sweet Marie,
    Sure, you'll never win the Farmers' Cup for me;
    And if YOU don't pull it through, faith, I'm done,
           and so are you,
    For I'll trade you off for glue, Sweet Marie.

Now, the colours that I chose for Sweet Marie
Were Lavender and Rose for Sweet Marie,
Och, but now, no thanks to you, sure I'm quite another hue,
For I'm only black and blue, Sweet Marie.
    Hould your hoult, Sweet Marie,
    If you bolt, Sweet Marie,
    Sure, you'll never win the Farmers' Cup for me.
    Every daisy in the dell ought to know me mighty well,
    For on every one I fell, Sweet Marie.

Now we're started for the Cup, my Sweet Marie,
Weight for age and owners up, my Sweet Marie,
Owners up just now I own, but the way you're waltzing roun'
Sure, 'twill soon be owners down, Sweet Marie.
    Hould your hoult, Sweet Marie;
    Pass the colt, Sweet Marie.
    Och, you've gone and lost the Farmers' Cup for me,
    You're a stayer too, I find: but you're not the
                  proper kind
    For you stay too far behind, Sweet Marie.

RAFFERTY'S RACIN' MARE

You've not seen Rafferty round this way?
He's a man with a broken hat,
His tie and his collar are all gone astray
And his coat for the matter of that!
We're racin' Rafferty round the place
Since Rafferty raced his mare,
He's a man with an anxious look on his face
And a partially murdered air!

    Chorus
    Oh! Rafferty's racin' mare,
    We met him at the fair,
    Says he "She'll win, so keep your tin,
    For backin' the racin' mare."
    Oh! Rafferty's racin' mare!
    We thanked him then and there,
    And every lad in Ballinafad
    Went backing the racin' mare.

I was the jockey they chose to ride—
And often the owner he sware
That there wasn't a leap in the earth too wide
To baffle the racin' mare.

Over hurdle and ditch she went like a witch,
Till she came where the water shone—
I gave her her head, but she stopped at it dead:
She stopped—and I went on!

> *Chorus*
> Oh! Rafferty's racin' mare—
> I whirtled through the air
> Like a beautiful bird, but never a word
> From Rafferty's racin' mare!

"Get up, you lad," says Ballinafad,
"You'll win the race for us yet."
But I didn't care for the look of the mare,
Nor the way that her legs were set.
Says they: "The horse'll stay the course,
She'll stay it—every foot."
"You're right," says I—"I don't deny
She'll stay just where she's put."

> *Chorus*
> Oh! Rafferty's racin' mare!
> We danced around her there,
> With stones and sticks, and bits o' bricks
> We hit her fair and square.
> Oh! Rafferty's racin' mare!
> The field they leapt it there,
> But on the brink she'd stand and—drink,
> Would Rafferty's racin' mare.

But where was Rafferty all the time?
Oh! Rafferty! he's the lad,
There in the ring—he stood like a king,
Cheerin' the mare like mad.
His brother was there, disguised, of course,
As a Roosian millionaire;
Giving the odds aginst every horse
And the longest aginst the mare.

Chorus
Oh! Rafferty's racin' mare!
'Twas more than we could bear,
When a bookie revealed
He was backin' the field,
Instead of the racin' mare.
We've got the day to spare,
We've got the millionaire;
And we're havin' a race around the place,
And Rafferty—he's the hare!

French was not long under the tutelage of Mr. Price, although, typically, he retained friendly contact with him for some time afterwards, as after a short time he took up an appointment with the Board of Works in Cavan and became engineer on a drainage scheme. This great event was commemorated in the family magazine which he had been running, in conjunction with the Godleys, from early days, and which, for a time, was continued to be run off on an old spirit duplicating machine, even when they had all left their respective homes. A. D. Godley, previously mentioned, to whom this is addressed, became in later years a noted scholar, and Public orator at Oxford; and was himself the author of classical light verse which, if more finely etched than French's, has not been remembered so well.

The full and original version of "The Inspector of Drains" has not been published before. A shortened version, with some of the words slightly altered, will be found in "Prose, Poems and Parodies of Percy French". It was still further shortened to three verses (marked*), and set to music for the first time by Eric Rogers for "The Golden Years".

Possibly some of the verses in the original form are repetitive and superfluous, but they are interesting as an example of the early work of W. P. French, and include a verse by Godley which inspired the effusion. The drawing is from French's own illustration of the original. The moustached figure on the left is his impression of himself at the time.

THE EFFUSION OF WILLIAM

INSPECTOR OF DRAINS

"E flumine fructus"
From drains gains

TO THE EDITOR

We heard with much regret that you
The Western Shores were going to
But now it seems you are to have an
Appointment on the "sewers" of Cavan
(From *Life and Letters of A. D. Godley*.)

The Local Inspector at Cavan in reply writes to Mr. G— of the XY Commission.

*Let others disport on American plains,
And rob the Redman of his hardly earned gains,
No tomahawk ever shall injure the brains
Of William the Local Inspector of Drains.

*He mounts his tall trap, gives his charger the reins
And gallops away through the green country lanes,
The Board pays the posting, the Balance remains
With William, the Local Inspector of Drains.

He plunges through marshes long haunted by cranes,
Quite heedless of how the dark bog-water stains;
Traducers assert that this ardour he feigns:
They little know William, Inspector of Drains.

He finds out the holding and what it contains
And maps out the system in furlongs and chains,
Then points out position for "minors" and "mains"—
Such wisdom has William, Inspector of Drains.

Of course he remains within doors if it rains
And wakes the piano's voluptuous strains,
And if of delay the bold tenant complains
He's sat on by William, Inspector of Drains.

Having been told that the board entertains
His case, the bold tenant declares that he "manes"
Not to be sat on by Inspector of Drains
Let them be English, *French*, Saxons, or Danes.

Offering whiskey; Cork's, Dublin's, Coleraine's,
He thinks to cajole the Inspector of Drains,
But his object in this he never attains
For William's true Irish, but always "La Reine's".

*'Tis an onerous post, but the writer refrains
From giving details of its pleasures and pains,
So, wishing you every success he remains
Yours Truly, the Local Inspector of Drains.

Mr. G— forwards the effusion of William to Mr. Le F.,
Commissioner of Public Works.

This copy of verses, the sender explains,
Must be sent back fortwith under heaviest pains,
Although the receiver might plead that he reigns
Supreme over all the Inspectors of Drains.

Mr. Le F. returns it and writes—

With thanks he returns (but a copy retains)
The verses, whose cleverness clearly contains
Proof positive what a large quontam of brains
Has William, the Local Inspector of Drains.

The Assistant Commissioner adds.

The Assistant Commissioner copies these strains,
Is officially angry, but kindly refrains,
From expressing more strongly the manner it pains
Him to learn how the time of Inspector of Drains
Is spent with fair maids in the green Cavan lanes,
While the Assistant Commissioner thinks that their brains,
Are engaged night and day in reporting on drains.
To the Assistant Commissioner nothing remains
But to state with what pleasure he always maintains
That, although there may be on their coats a few stains
There are none on the names of Inspectors of Drains.

The correspondence must have somehow fallen into other hands for—

> The Assistant Commissioner's daughter maintains
> That Inspectors who dawdle indoors when it rains
> Making impartial love to the Betsys and Janes
> Are not worthy to rank as Inspectors of Drains.
>
> She thinks it most doubtful a red-man would deign
> To blunt a new tomahawk over the brain
> —Or rather the place where it ought to have lain
> Of a person whose intellect's spent in a drain.
>
> She pities the quasi-woe-begone swains
> And suggests that they take the uttermost pains;
> Not notice the conquests that William attains
> Fair maids will soon tire of Inspector of Drains.

We are afraid this young lady must be jealous. The chief is full of admiration, and writes there on William's effusion,—

> One hint I would venture before the thing wanes,
> That our Chairman should see these most exquisite strains,
> Little thinks he what fancy could shoot from the brains
> Of one who descends to the depths of the Drains.
> *De profundis clamavi!* but no one disdains
> What the pen of the poet so clearly explains,
> And a Cynic is he who objects or complains
> Of the Idylls of William, Inspector of Drains.

Underlying some irony in this "effusion" is good-humoured acceptance of engineering as a career, although there is little indication that he ever regarded it as being more than a means of making a living somehow. As may be noted from the text there had been a family suggestion that Willie would go to America following his training with Mr. Price. Then, as now, it was the land of opportunity, with vast schemes for opening up the west where a young engineer might make his fortune; or alternatively leave his scalp on the belt of a redman making a last stand for independent existence. If the American idea had been carried through, French might have written something like "Steamboat Bill" instead of "The Mountains of Mourne", but fortunately he stayed in Ireland and Cavan became his home for seven years. It was possibly the happiest time of his life. He quickly became popular in many of the surrounding houses with his musical talent, his banjo and his songs, and it wasn't long before he was organizing a nigger minstrel troupe—The Kinniepottle Komics— among the young bloods of the county and town.

Nigger minstrelsy was at that time a vogue—right up to the minute stuff as the "beat" might be today—and Willie, as witness his addiction to the banjo, and the accompaniment of bones and tambourine provided by the Godleys in younger days, had been an early enthusiast: in fact, before he turned more definitely to Irish ballads he wrote several mock plantation songs.

These have not survived, but one, "The Hoodoo" used later for a show in London, but possibly written earlier, was successful.

"THE HOODOO"

When de stars begin to peep and de moon am shinin'
Into our cabin homes we creep
Me and Lindy Loo,
Out of his cave der comes de Hoodoo
Yes! der comes de creepy crawly Hoodoo—
And if a chile ain't in his bed
De Hoodoo'll catch him sure!

Chorus:

Whisper low!
When twilight shades are falling
Pull de clo' around de curly head
To and fro I hear de Hoodoo calling:—
"Are dere any little picaninnies who am not in bed?"

Once der was a wicked little girl
Not like ma Lindy!
Flat-foot niggeress name o' Sal
Said "I don't suppose
Dat der is anything like de Hoodoo
Shouldn't run away from it like you do!"
Where has she gone dat naughty little girl?
Only de Hoodoo knows!

    Chorus:
    Whisper low! etc.

Work at night for dose we lub—
Dat scares de Hoodoo!
Den him sings like a turtle dove cooin' all night long,
Now dat we're one dat's what we do do,
Guess it's what I see ma Lindy Loo do
Wish for de little one dat we've got
Singin' de whole night thro'.

    Chorus:
    So I know,
    When twilight shades are falling
    Comes the foe de picaninnies dread,
    Soft and slow I hear de Hoodoo calling:—
    "Are dere any little picaninnies who am not in bed?"

Through his work as Inspector of Drains he again came into close contact with the farming community. With the natural, easy ways by which he seemed able to suit himself to any company he soon overcame any ingrained suspicion of his "Trinity" accent, and having been accepted on easy terms by them, began reporting their doings and misdoings and romances in songs which had a real sympathy for them and only the natural exaggerations of their own conversation to give a humorous twist. The people of the countryside always accepted him as "wan" o' themselves, and he was usually far happier with them than in a drawingroom.

Enamoured of the countryside through which duty took him daily on a bicycle or in a pony and trap he took up painting seriously for the first time (one presumes the drains sometimes had to wait) and the delicate browns and blues and greens of his water colours took several prizes at exhibitions when sent to Dublin and elsewhere. In fact, some of his finest paintings date from the Cavan period, as well as two of his very best songs—one gay one written at the time, and one with the memory of twenty years behind it. He would never make better songs than "Phil the Fluther's Ball" and "Come Back, Paddy Reilly".

Of these songs, so typical of his stay in Cavan, Phil the Fluther reached the public the year of his return to Dublin, although it had probably been sung at many a party and concert before that, but Paddy Reilly did not appear until 1912. Phil the Fluther was a real-life character, occupying a small holding in Leitrim, who was known to the Godleys. It is apparently true that when times were hard and he was pressed for the rent he would hold a dance in his little house, when he would "toot the flute"; a friend would "twiddle the fiddle" and other friends would "pay at the door" so that the evil day might be postponed. Apparently Phil's "Rent-parties" became quite a feature, so that the walls of the little house sometimes nearly burst at the seams.

PHIL THE FLUTHER'S BALL

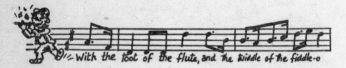

With the toot of the flute, and the twiddle of the fiddle-o

Have you heard of Phil the Fluther, of the town of Ballymuck?
The times were going hard with him, in fact the man was broke
So he just sent out a notice to his neighbours, one and all
As to how he'd like their company that evening at a ball.
And when writin' out he was careful to suggest to them,
That if they found a hat of his convanient to the dure,
The more they put in, whenever he requested them
The better would the music be for battherin' the flure.

Chorus:
With the toot of the flute,
And the twiddle of the fiddle, O;
Hopping in the middle, like a herrin' on the griddle, O.
Up! down, hands aroun'
Crossing to the wall.
Oh! hadn't we the gaiety at Phil the Fluther's Ball.

There was Misther Denis Dogherty, who kep' the runnin' dog;
There was little crooked Paddy, from the Tiraloughett bog;
There was boys from every Barony, and girls from ev'ry "art"
And the beautiful Miss Bradys, in a private ass an' cart,
And along with them came bouncing Mrs. Cafferty,
Little Micky Mulligan was also to the fore,
Rose, Suzanne, and Margaret O'Rafferty,
The flower of Ardmagullion, and the pride of Pethravore.

First, little Micky Mulligan got up to show them how,
And then the Widda' Cafferty steps out and makes her bow,
I could dance you off your legs, sez she, as sure as you are born,
If ye'll only make the piper play "The hare was in the corn."
So Phil plays up to the best of his ability,
The lady and the gentleman begin to do their share;
Faith then Mick it's you that has agility:
Begorra Mrs. Cafferty, yer leppin' like a hare!

Then Phil the Fluther tipped a wink to little Crooked Pat,
I think it's nearly time sez he, for passin' round the hat
So Paddy pass'd the caubeen round, and looking mighty cute
Sez, "Ye've got to pay the piper when he toothers on the flute"
Then all joined in wid the greatest joviality,
Covering the buckle, and the shuffle, and the cut;
Jigs were danced, of the very finest quality,
But the Widda' bet the company at "handling the fut."

There is a sure touch of nostalgia about Paddy Reilly and
Ballyjamesduff. Some say that he accepted a challenge to write
a song featuring "Ballyjamesduff"; a small town about twelve
miles south-east of Cavan. Reilly is a very common name around
these parts, and at least part of the background may have been

suggested by a tablet on the bridge of Finea—a crossroads
seventeen miles south of Cavan on the road to Mullingar—
commemorating a battle in which numerous members of the
Reilly clan were engaged.

The more likely origin of the song is that when Percy French
returned to the Cavan scenes of his youth many years later he
found that the man who used to drive him in a horse and car
from Ballyjamesduff station in earlier days, a great character whom
he had looked forward to seeing again, had emigrated to America.
French missed him and wrote a song to his memory.

COME BACK PADDY REILLY

The Garden of Eden has vanished they say,
But I know the lie of it still;
Just turn to the left at the bridge of Finea,
And stop when half-way to Cootehill.
'Tis there I will find it; I know sure enough.
When fortune has come to me call.
Oh! the grass it is green around Ballyjamesduff.
And the blue sky is over it all;
And tones that are tender, and tones that are gruff
Are whispering over the sea,
"Come back, Paddy Reilly, to Ballyjamesduff,
Come home, Paddy Reilly, to me".

My mother once told me that when I was born,
The day that I first saw the light,
I looked down the street on that very first morn,
And gave a great crow of delight.
Now most new born babies appear in a huff,
And start with a sorrowful squall
But I knew I was born in Ballyjamesduff,
And that's why I smiled on them all.
The baby's a man, now he's toil-worn and tough,
Still, whispers come over the sea,
"Come back, Paddy Reilly, to Ballyjamesduff,
"Come home, Paddy Reilly, to me".

The night that we danced by the light of the moon,
Wid Phil to the fore with his flute.
When Phil threw his lip over "Come again soon"
He'd dance the foot out o' yer boot!
The day that I took long Magee by the scruff,
For slanderin' Rosie Kilrain,
Then marchin' him straight out of Ballyjamesduff
Assisted him into a drain.
Oh, sweet are me dreams, as the dudeen I puff,
Of whisperings over the sea,
"Come back, Paddy Reilly, to Ballyjamesduff,
Come home, Paddy Reilly, to me."

I've loved the young women of every land—
That always came easy to me,
Just barrin' the belles of the Black-a-moor brand,
And the chocolate shapes of Feegee.
But that sort of love is a moonshiny stuff,
And never will addle me brain.
For the bells will be ringin' in Ballyjamesduff,
For me and me Rosie Kilrain!
And all through their glamour, their gas, and their guff,
A whisper comes over the sea,
"Come back, Paddy Reilly, to Ballyjamesduff,
Come home, Paddy Reilly to me."

Encore Verse

I've struck oil at last! I've struck work, and I vow,
I've struck some remarkable clothes.
I've struck a policeman for saying that now,
I'd go back on me beautiful Rose,
The belles they may blarney, the boys they may bluff,
But this I will always maintain,
No place in the world like Ballyjamesduff,
No guril like Rosie Kilrain.
I've paid for my passage, the sea may be rough,
But borne on each breeze there will be,
"Come back, Paddy Reilly, to Ballyjamesduff,
Come back, Paddy Reilly, to me."

The second song to be published appeared in 1888 while he
was still in the North, and told in a jocose way the adventures of
one Andy McElroe while "sojering" in the Sudan. It was written
in collaboration with "J. Ross", in other words, Sir John Ross,
who held a legal position in the North at that time.

ANDY McELROE

My brother Andy said that for a soldier he would go,
So great excitement came upon the house of McElroe
My father sold the bog hole to equip him for the war,
My mother sold the cushions of her Sunday jauntin' car;
And when brave Andy reached the front, 'twas furious work he
    made
They appointed him a private in the Crocodile Brigade,
The sound of Andy's battle-cry struck terror through the foe,
His foot was on the desert, and his name was McElroe.

Chorus

At least, that's what the letter said that came across the foam
To Andy's anxious relatives, awaiting him at home;
The papers say he ran away, whene'er he met the foe,
But that was quite unlike the style of Andy McElroe.

One morning brave Lord Wolseley for a battle felt inclined;
But all could see the General had something on his mind;
Sez he, "My staff, 'twere dangerous to face yon deadly foe,
Unless we're sure that quite prepared is Andy McElroe."
Then Andy cried, "I'm here, my Lord, and ready for the fray"
"Advance then," cried Lord Wolseley, "and let every trumpet bray"
Then England, Ireland, Scotland, rolled together on the foe,
But far ahead of everyone rushed Andy McElore.

> *Chorus*
> At least, that's what the letter said that came across the foam
> To Andy's anxious relatives, awaiting him at home.
> The Government despatches had another tale—but no!
> We won't believe a word against brave Andy McElroe.

The Mahdi had gone up a tree, a spyglass in his eye,
To see his Paynim chivalry the Northern prowess try:
But soon he saw a form of dread, and cried in tones of woe,
"Be jabers let me out of this—there's Andy McElroe"
Then down he hurried from his tree, and straight away he ran,
To keep appointments, as he said, in distant Kordofan,
And fled those Arab soldiery like sand siroccos blow,
Pursued (with much profanity) by Andy McElore.

> *Chorus*
> At least, that's what he told us when returning o'er the foam
> To greet his anxious relatives, awaiting him at home.
> So sing the song of triumph, and let all your bumpers flow,
> In honour of our countryman, brave Andrew McElroe.

In having "Andy" published French at least showed that he
had learned a lesson from the "Abdulla" episode, for this and
many succeeding songs were published by the reputable Dublin
firm, Pigotts.

Early in the following year another song with a military setting
saw the light and was in time to become one of the best-known;
but this—"Shlathery's Mounted Fut"—had a different background. It describes the adventures of a locally raised band of
Irish "volunteers".

SHLATHERY'S MOUNTED FUT.

DOWN FROM THE MOUNTAINS CAME THE SQUADRONS AND PLATOONS

You've heard o' Julius Caesar, an' the great Napoleon too,
An' how the Cork Militia beat the Turks at Waterloo,
But there's a page of glory that, as yet, remains uncut,
An' that's the Martial story o' the Shlathery's Mounted Fut.
This gallant corps was organised by Shlathery's eldest son.
A single-minded poacher, wid a double-breasted gun;
An' many a head was opened, aye, an' many an eye was shut,
Whin practisin' manoeuvres in the Shlathery's Mounted Fut.

> *Chorus*
> An' down from the mountain came the squadrons an'
>   platoons,
> Four-an'-twinty fightin' min, an' a couple o' sthout
>   gossoons,
> An' whin we marched behind the dhrum to patriotic tunes,
> We felt that fame would gild the name o' Shlathery's
>   Light Dragoons.

Well, first we reconnoithered round O'Sullivan's Shebeen—
It used to be "The Shop House," but we call it, "The Canteen,"
But there we saw a notice which the bravest heart unnerved—
"All liquor must be settled for before the dhrink is served."
So on we marched, but soon again each warrior's heart grew pale,
For risin' high in front o' us we saw the County Jail;
And when the army faced about, 'twas just in time to find
A couple o' stout policemin had surrounded us behind.

Chorus

> Still, from the mountains came the squadrons and platoons,
> Four-an'-twinty fightin' min, an' a couple o' sthout
> > gossoons;
> Says Shlathery, "We must circumvent these bludgeonin'
> > bosthoons,
> Or else it sames they'll take the names o' Shlathery's
> > Light Dragoons."

"We'll cross the ditch," our leader cried, "an' take the foe in flank,"
But yells of consthernation here arose from every rank,
For posted high upon a tree we very plainly saw,
"Threspassers prosecuted, in accordance wid' the law."
"We're foiled!" exclaimed bould Shlathery, "here ends our grand
> campaign,
'Tis merely throwin' life away to face that mearin' drain,
I'm not as bold as lions, but I'm braver nor a hin,
An' he that fights and runs away will live to fight agin."

Chorus

> An' back to the mountains went the squadrons and
> > platoons,
> Four-an'-twinty fightin' min an' a couple o' sthout
> > gossoons;
> The band was playing cautiously their patriotic tunes;
> To sing the fame, if rather lame o' Shlathery's
> > Light Dragoons.

These are comic songs, and too much significance should not
be attached to them, but the fact that these two martial numbers
tell of different kinds of "sojering" as related to Ireland is of some
interest when viewed against Percy French's background.

Andy McElroe, in the first song, is an Irishman serving in the
British Army—a career which may seem anomalous when the
frequent "agitations" against British Rule are considered, but one

which was followed by many a young Irishman in search of
adventure, or seeing the world, or even a job, over a period of a
hundred years or more.

It was not a new theme in Balladry. Several ballads of Napoleonic
times, from native hands, used the theme of the Irish soldier
abroad. A person of French's upbringing, while considering himself as a true Irishman, would certainly see nothing unusual in
McElroe serving the Queen ("For William's true Irish but always
'La Reine's'") and in fact he repeated this theme several times—
in Cornelius Burke, The Killyran Wrackers, and Soldiers Three,
for instance. These "heroes" are usually out for divilment,
with rather cynical ideas about being loyal to anyone but themselves. On the other hand, he, in common with a great number
of people of all classes, could not conceive that Irishmen could
organise and control an army of their own, such as Bould Shlathery
attempted to do. Nobody could see ahead to the events of the
next thirty years.

There is nothing political in any of this. Admittedly, French
moved in a circle which would not be, in the nature of things,
nationally minded, but he himself just was not politically inclined
at all: as his cousin R. B. D. French afterwards wrote "Does one
analyse the comic songs of so unpolitical a man?" It certainly is
wiser not to read motives into them when they were written
merely to amuse and entertain. Percy French loved Ireland and the
Irish people, and never consciously wrote them down at any time.
What he does in these songs is to express generally accepted views
rather than give his own.

In Cavan Willie fell in love for the first time. The girl was
Ettie Armitage-Moore of Arnmore and her father was Lord
Annesley's agent. Her sister Priscilla later became Lady Annesley.
To the latter marriage there would have been little objection,
since the family had social ambitions, but when French married
Ettie in Dublin in 1890 he did so despite opposition from her
people: they considered his way of life and prospects a little
insecure. Their point of view could possibly be understood for,
when the drains scheme at Cavan finished in January of 1889 and
he found himself out of work Percy finally gave up engineering
and accepted the post of editor to a new comic magazine.

This was called *The Jarvey* and the position was offered to him by R. J. Macredy, a well-known Dublin Journalist, who also ran other magazines, including *The Irish Cyclist*. Macredy himself was a noted racing cyclist. French had been sending fairly regular contributions of humorous articles and light verse to him and other editors for he had never really lost touch with literary activity even while in Cavan.

Soon he was well and truly circulating in the literary and musical society of the capital, but at the end of 1890 the short-lived life to *The Jarvey* ended, and he was at the cross-roads again.

The following year, 1891, was to be a fateful one for him. Early in that year he met and began his collaboration with the little Dublin musician, Houston Collisson. At the time of their first meeting Collisson was a young musician, ten years junior to French, but had already become well-known as organist, pianist and the organizer of a unique series of concerts in Dublin and the provinces.

Together they wrote an Irish musical comedy, the first of its type, called "The Knight of the Road" (see Appendix II), later to be known as "The Irish Girl". For this French provided the lyrics and the dialogue assisted by a man called Brendan Stewart, and Collisson wrote the music. "The Knight of the Road" was produced at the Queen's Theatre, Dublin at Easter of that year and was a great success, playing to packed houses for a week. The story was taken from an old book called *Irish Rogues and Raparees*. It is an excellent piece in its style and period—a little dated now in parts, but one which, with judicious re-alignment of the dialogue here and there, could well bear the possibility of revival.

With this collaboration French found himself in the hurly-burly of show business and, despite the erratic zig-zag manner of his participation, he was to remain in it for the rest of his life. He continued to write articles and started to give lessons in painting, so the future of his family, soon to be increased, seemed to be a little more secure, when, unexpectedly, the greatest of blows fell. Ettie, his "Ray of Sunshine" died almost on the anniversary of their wedding while giving birth to their child, and her baby survived for only a few weeks after her.

GORTNAMONA

Long, long ago in the woods of Gortnamona,
I thought the birds were singing in the Blackthorn tree;
But oh! it was my heart that was ringing, ringing, ringing,
With the joy that you were bringing O my love, to me.

Long, long ago, in the woods of Gortnamona,
I thought the wind was sighing round the Blackthorn tree;
But oh! it was the banshee that was crying, crying, crying,
And I knew my love was dying far across the sea.

Now if you go through the woods of Gortnamona,
You hear the raindrops creeping through the Blackthorn tree.
But oh! it is the tears I am weeping, weeping, weeping,
For the loved one that is sleeping far away from me.

These verses were not composed, as has sometimes been
thought, to mark the death of his little "Ray of Sunshine", but
were one of a number of a rather more serious nature which he
wrote from time to time more to supply an inner satisfaction than
from a commercial viewpoint; but they were linked most effectively
with this sad event in a radio biography "The Last Troubador",
which Radio Éireann first put on the air at Christmas of 1956,
and it does not seem out of place to connect them with it here.
In French's life they were "words without song", but Phil Green
set them to music in 1958.

After his wife's death, French had to face the sober realisation
that he was thirty-seven years old, and that the first bursting joy
of manhood was over. In many ways he had not ceased to be a boy,
and somewhere inside him, it was doubtful if he ever would, but
some of the sadness which is inseparable from life had reached
him. Sorrow had touched Willie French, as so often it does with
all of us, when everything, even through the cheerfully muddled
pattern of his life, had seemed to be going right now he was on his
own again. Most of his scanty savings had been lost sometime
before by the failure of a distillery in which he had invested them,
so the necessity to make a living became a very real one. *The Jarvey*
had failed: there seemed no regular journalistic work of a similar

nature in view, and at any rate his lack of management capacity would have become sufficiently apparent through his short-lived experience with that magazine. Painting, and the teaching of painting could only promise a small return, not sufficient for his immediate needs, so to the gratitude of all those who love the songs of Percy French, there was only one alternative. He turned to the stage.

While *The Jarvey* had been in existence he had seen a good deal of Richard Orpen, a rising young architect, who had contributed a number of drawings to the magazine, and had illustrated the covers for some of French's songs. Their families were friends. They formed a friendship, such as he had with the Godleys, and put together a number of items to entertain their friends. French, who didn't quite know where his new career was leading him, and was trying this and that, hit on the idea that, with additional material, these could be made into a topical revue; so "Dublin-up-to-date", with sketches, recitations, and a comic lecture on Dublin with magic lantern slides came into being.

There were several new songs, specially written.

MATHEW HANNIGAN'S AUNT

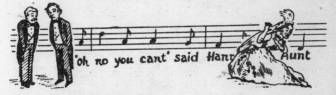

Oh, Mat Hannigan had an aunt,
    An uncle too, likewise:
But in this chant, 'tis Hannigan's aunt
    I mean to eulogize.
    For when young lovers came
    And axed her to be their's
Mat Hannigan's aunt took each gallant
    And fired him down the stairs.

Chorus:

So here's a health to Hannigan's aunt!
    I'll tell you the reason why,
She always had things dacent
    In the Hannigan family:
A platther and can for every man,
    "What more do the quality want?
"You've yer bit and yer sup what's cockin' yees up!"
    Sez Mathew Hannigan's aunt.

Oh, she never could raise her voice,
    She never was known to scold,
But when Hannigan's aunt sed, "No, you can't,"
    You did what you were told;
And if anyone answered back,
    Oh, then his hair she'd comb,
"For all I want," sez Hannigan's aunt,
    "Is peace in our happy home."

Chorus:

So here's a health, etc.

Oh, when she went to Court,
    The A-de-congs in vain
Would fume and rant, for Hannigan's Aunt
    Said, "Boy let go me thrain!"
And when the Lard Leftinant
    A kiss on her brow would imprint!
"Oh no, you can't," said Hannigan's Aunt
    "Widout me pa's consint."

Chorus:

So here's a health etc.

Oh, 'tis often we'd praise her up,
    We'd laud her to the sky,
We'd all descant on Hannigan's Aunt,
    And hope she never would die.
But still I'd like to add—
    If Hannigan isn't about—
That whin we plant Mat Hannigan's Aunt,
    We won't be too put out.

Chorus:
So here's a health etc.

SOLDIERS THREE

We soldiers are a terror to the foe, boys,
And though I'm on the shelf,
Such a warrior was I when I let my rifle fly,
I've often been a terror to myself,
'Twas just before the battle,
We heard the sergeant say;
"Be sure you come, when you hear the drum"
We came—we came away.

    Chorus:
    For we don't like to hear the bullets rattle in the battle
    And we don't like to hear the cannons roar—any more—
    But we'll gather on the gory field of battle,
    When the cruel war is o'er.

There was me and Hector Mooney and O'Hara,
Three soldiers bold and gay,
And we swore with one accord we would never draw a sword,
But we'd always draw our pay.
When the order came for marching,
And to get into fighting trim,
Beneath our breath as we marched to death
We sung the soldier's hymn.

    Chorus.

They told us we were bound for death or glory,
So we kept a sharp look out;
Says Mooney, "I declare that death is everywhere
But the glory never seems to be about."
We were not in front, boys,
When the army charged along,
But beneath a cock of hay on that memorial day,
You might have heard this song.

Chorus.

Then me, and Hector Mooney, and O'Hara,
We all marched home again,
And we tell about the fight and the deeds of might,
We did in our last campaign.
You see this long red scar, lads,
I've got behind my ear,
It was not a sabre's edge, it was dashin' thro' a hedge
With the foemen in the rear.

Chorus.

Richard Orpen did a sketching turn during the performance,
and, in a later edition of the show, his younger brother, Billy,
then only a schoolboy, but later to become the famous artist
Sir William, assisted in one of the sketches. Both brothers did
lightning sketches during the interval—which could nowadays
be worth very much more than the 6d. charged, to anyone who
had the wit to keep them.

This entertainment was so popular that its fame reached beyond
the capital, and they were approached to appear at places up and
down the country. Richard could not travel—his duties as a
young architect tied him to Dublin, and at any rate he did not
intend to make the stage a career; and Billy Orpen (never really
an integral part of the show) was too young, so Percy French
took over Richard's sketching act and decided to go it alone.
These were the circumstances giving birth to the remarkable
solo performance of later years; but at first there were only a few
scattered engagements, suggested by friends. The important
thing was that many people now heard Percy French and his

banjo for the first time, although the idea of making a permanent success out of this pleasant life probably never entered his head.

Collisson, however, had other ideas, and if French could not see the potential value of their partnership the busy little doctor certainly could for he kept deluging the uncertain path of the wanderer with reminders of future plans and in particular with ideas for a successor to "The Knight of the Road". He might get no reply for weeks, and then a succession of lyrics would arrive, written on the back of a postcard, or some old envelope which happened to be handy.

These two, who shared a large part of their experiences and talents through the next three decades, were different in many ways. Physically both were small—French was 5′4″ and Collisson was even smaller, but temperamentally they were extremes. French was easy-going and took life as it came. As long as he could make enough to keep going and carry on with his songs and paintings he never developed driving force or ambition enough to want to be a successful anything at all. His happy-go-lucky ways were often trying to friends and associates who were trying to help him, but it was almost impossible to be annoyed with him, although people were often exasperated; and in the middle of any fuss, Percy French remained serene and unruffled; thinking, maybe, of that golden light on the trees beyond the river, or wondering if a song could be made of what McGrath had said to Young Eileen, if only these pleasant people would get out of the way.

EILEEN OGE

Eileen Oge, and that the darlin's name is,
Through the Barony her features they were famous,
If we loved her who is there to blame us,
For wasn't she the Pride of Petravore.
But her beauty made us all so shy,
Not a man could look her in the eye.
Boys, oh boys! sure that's the reason why
We're in mournin' for the Pride of Petravore.

Chorus: Eileen Oge, me heart is growin' grey
           Ever since the day you wander'd far away
           Eileen Oge, there's good fish in the say,
           But there's no one like the Pride of Petravore.

Friday at the Fair of Ballintubber,
Eileen met McGrath, the cattle jobber,
I'd like to set me mark upon the robber,
For he stole away the Pride of Petravore.
He never seem'd to see the girl at all,
Even when she ogle'd him underneath her shawl,
Lookin' big and masterful, when she was looking small,
Most provokin' for the Pride of Petravore.

         Chorus.

So it went as it was in the beginning,
Eileen Oge was bent upon the winning.
Big McGrath contentedly was grinning,
Being courted by the Pride of Petravore.
Sez he, "I know a girl that could knock you into fits"
At that Eileen nearly lost her wits.
The upshot of the ruction was that now the robber sits,
With his arm around the Pride of Petravore.

         Chorus.

Boys oh, boys! with fate 'tis hard to grapple,
Of my eye 'tis Eileen was the apple.
And now to see her walkin' to the chapel
Wid the hardest featured man in Petravore.
And, now, me boys, this is all I have to say,
When you do your courtin' make no display,
If you want them to run after you just walk the other way,
For they're mostly like the Pride of Petravore.

         Chorus.

French's amiability was of a quiet, even reserved kind. He liked the company of his own friends, but not of large parties. but the congratulations of old and new friends after a concert was half the evening to Collisson and made his little figure swell with appreciation. His manner was old maidenish without being effeminate, and he had some of the natural conceit of a professional who took his work as a musician seriously—but he too had the grace to laugh at himself. He recalled the lady who enquired, in all seriousness, whether the concert was to be comprised of only his music, as "I thought we were going to have some good music too!" Another dear old soul congratulated him on his performance of "Maguire's Motor Bike"—"It was so delightfully vulgar". One wonders what the dear old lady would have thought of some modern lyrics.

MAGUIRE'S MOTOR BIKE

(A Tragedy in Four Acts)

It was Mick Maguire made it,
All alone, and all unaided,
For I tell you that a bhoy was Mick.
And for divilment and murther,
Sure you needn't go no further
Than the bicycle he called "The kill-me-quick."
The gear-case was a kettle
Made of good Britannia metal,
As good as you would buy in any shop,
And whin once you set it goin'
Faith there never was no knowin'
Where Maguire's Motor Bicycle would stop.

> *Chorus:*
> But the bike's allright,
> Not a bit it matter'd
> Oh! the bike's allright,
> And none the worse for wear.
> Oh! the bike's allright,
> The rider might be shattered.
> But the bike's allright,
> So Maguire doesn't care.

'Twould come whizzin' round a corner
And before you'd time to warn her
'Twould be through some poor old woman like a knife,
And Flynn the undertaker,
Said to Mike (that was the maker),
That he never was so busy in his life,
He'd lind it to relations
From whom he'd expectations,
And to folks for whom he didn't care.
Then Mick would say with sorrow
"There'll be funerals to-morrow,"
And it somehow always happen'd that there were.

Chorus:

But the bike's allright,
His uncle tried to cycle,
Oh! the bike's allright,
And none the worse for ware.
The bike's allright,
The money went to Michael!
Oh! the bike's allright
So Maguire doesn't care.

They tried him for manslaughter,
But the case would not hold water,
For Maguire proved an alibi each time,
And not a one could shake him,
And divil a one could make him
In any ways accessory to crime.
They were gettin' quite alarmed,
And so a plot was formed,
A conspiracy they thought would never fail,
So they sought the level crossin'
When the "nine o'clock" was passin'
And they laid it gintly down upon the rail.

Chorus:

Oh! the bike's allright,
Not a bit it mattered.
Oh! the bike's allright,
And none the worse for wear.
The bike's allright,
The nine o'clock was scatter'd,
But the bike's allright,
So Maguire doesn't care.

Oh! the town was in a fury,
For at the next grand jury,
They were fined for an attempt to wreck the train
And out of the entire lot
'Twas only Mick Maguire got
Away from out the court without a stain.
So they held a monster meetin'
For the purpose of debatin'
A way to put the cycle on the shelf,
So at last it was decided,
And assinted, and provided,
That Maguire takes a ride on it himself.

Chorus:

The bike's allright,
Maguire tried to ride it,
Oh! the bike's allright,
Just as it was before.
The bike's allright,
They buried it beside him.
The bike's allright,
But Maguire he's no more.

W. A. Houston Collisson was born in 1865 of a good family in reduced circumstances, and while his early wish was to enter the Church conditions and an astonishing early talent directed his life towards music. He was a Church organist at sixteen in Trim: obtained his Bachelor of Music degree when nineteen and went on to take his doctorate when only twenty-five, having in the meantime been organist and choir-master at Bray and Rathfarnham. He started the "Popular Concerts" in Dublin in 1885, bringing really good artists from Ireland and abroad to take part in them, and subsequently organized these concerts of high-class music in different centres, such as Belfast, Cork and Derry. He even brought them to London. During this time he built up quite a reputation in the difficult art of accompaniment. This, and a certain amount of composition for the piano, had been his life until his quite considerable ambitions in the world of music brought him into close contact with Percy French in 1891.

Perhaps the greatest difference between the two men was that French never really took entertaining seriously as a profession, despite the fact that he worked hard at it. It all seemed to "just happen" with Percy French! Carefully rehearsed jokes sounded as if he had just thought of them, and his work had the air of a family party. Collisson, mentally more professional, liked everything to happen as planned. When they performed together Collisson, who had a pleasant light tenor voice, usually sang the songs while French sketched and told stories.

The further Irish opera which succeeded "The Knight of the Road" was "Strongbow" which like its predecessor went on at the Queen's Theatre, Dublin at Easter of 1892, but it did not have a great success.

One is unable to really judge their second work together since it was never printed and the manuscript has not come to light, but the subject would appear to have been somewhat heavy for writers who required lightness to achieve their best effects. But though "Strongbow" was not a success financially, it had one result which was an important influence on the life of the author. Essentially a family man who liked the quiet peace and companionship of a home he had, despite his active experimentation in the theatre, been lonely since the death of his first wife, Ettie, and now in the cast of "Strongbow" he was to meet somebody who would not only take her place, but be his guide and mentor for twenty-five years.

The casts of these musical-comedies were largely amateur, recruited from the friends of French, Collisson and others who mixed with musical circles in Dublin, and among those brought into the chorus of this show was a girl called Helen May Sheldon, then in her early twenties. She had been a school friend of one of the cast, and was on holidays with her in Ireland. Miss Sheldon came from Burmington House, near Shipston-on-Stour in Warwickshire, and the friendship which started as a result of "Strongbow" culminated in what was to be a happy marriage two years later, in 1894.

By then there had been a musical Comedietta called "Midsummer Madness" in 1893, with music by Collisson, which was a success and continued to be performed in whole, or in part, around Dublin for some years. It was in three parts, in one of which Collisson appeared as "Little Lord Faultyboy" dressed in velvet suit and lace collar; and another part was French's solo turn, now being established in the pattern which he was to use, with varying material, over many years.

He now started touring in earnest, with the needs of a new home to spur him on, and soon the name of "W. P. French" was a familiar and popular one on boards all over Ireland.

The solo performance was not a new idea as it had been popular from at least the time of French's predecessor in ballad writing, Samuel Lover, earlier in the century; and there were, or had been, such performers as the older Val Vousden, Willie Lee, and Claude Duval. George Grossmith, the great star of the Savoy

Operas, was probably most famous of the day with his "Piano and I", and French was a great admirer of his. When Grossmith died in 1912 he wrote an effective and touching tribute in verse. There had, according to Graves, been a suggestion at one time that they might collaborate, but this came to nothing.

None of them, however, could display the wide versatility which French displayed as all the facets of his talent and personality gradually blended to form his distinctive two hour performance. He could write songs and sing them to his own accompaniment; give his own recitations, touching or humorous as the case might be; tell stories in a manner which made the most ridiculous tales seem true. While "telling the tale" he sketched in coloured chalk on large sheets of paper—often illustrating the story with a drawing and then turning it upside down, when to his apparent surprise, it had become something else. Apart from these upside down sketches, which became quite a feature, he developed all sorts of artistic tricks—such as producing quite beautiful "smoke-pictures" on plates by merely using the smoke from a candle. Taken in all it was a unique performance which gained its greatest strength from the gentle but compelling personality of its originator.

French had one other trait common to all the great performers —he could be funny without being vulgar. This does not mean to say, however, that he never gave offence. There was, to give an instance, the case of the Cooneys. One night, just as a concert in a small town in the midlands of Ireland was about to commence, a large lady, rather more over-dressed than the occasion warranted, followed by several large daughters (rather more under-dressed than the occasion warranted) trooped in and settled in their reserved places in the front row. They were the family of a local merchant, nouveau-riche. It was the fashion to attend a performance by the now well-known entertainer, and they were determined to be there. He sang his first number, and at the end of it the whole convoy rose and sailed out again, headed by Mamma, like a Spanish galleon in full sail in her indignation; to the accompaniment of a hysterically applauding audience, who saw more to the joke than the singer did. The reception puzzled Willie French. This was the number:

THE NIGHT MISS COONEY ELOPED

Oh! boys, have ye heard of the Cooneys?
Their ways would have filled ye with dread,
They wouldn't leave cards on the Rooneys,
An' cut Patsy Gallagher dead.
They even looked down on the polis,
An' held a militiaman cheap.
So the family felt that their pride got a welt
When Miss Cooney eloped with the sweep.

> *Chorus:*
> Ould Cooney was tearin' his hair,
> An' said he'd not stay in the place;
> Mrs. Cooney she lepp'd off her chair,
> And said, "Twas a dyin' disgrace!"
> Young Cooney said he didn't care,
> But he sat in the corner an' moped;
> There was t'under and turf in the air, ye may swear,
> On the night that Miss Cooney eloped.

Says Cooney, "She's none o' me daughter,
And I won't have a sweep for me son;
If I meet them on land or on water,
I'll knock their two heads into one;"
Says the son, "Though he's famed as a fighter,
His death I will surely effect!"
But in this compact they lost sight of the fact
That the sweep would be sure to object.

Now the sweep was a terror to rassle,
And as to his fightin'—oh, there!
He always was king o' the castle,
At weddin' or wakin', or fair,
But, of course, wid the creme-de-la-cramers
He socially wasn't in touch—
As a sweep he would go to their houses, you know,
But was only admitted as such.

While they were abusin' the vill'in,
An' the daughter, through thick an' through thin,
An' swearin' she'd not have a shillin'—
The bride an' the bridegroom stepped in.
An' he lifted his fist up and shook it,
"I've married your daughter," he said,
"So hand out the dower—and if ye look sour,
Be gomis! I'll have ye for dead!"

Chorus:

So ould Cooney cried out, "Lave it there,
All we want is contentment an' peace;
Mrs. Cooney sat down on her chair,
An' says she, "You've an illigant face!"
Young Cooney said he didn't care,
It was better by far than he'd hoped.
Oh! the stream of good-will it would turn a mill
On the night that Miss Cooney eloped!

What Willie did not know was that this was the Cooney family, and that mama's strenuous attempts to have them accepted by the "County" with a display of newly-acquired wealth had recently been somewhat marred when one of the daughters ran away with a labourer; so that his song was more relevant to the occasion than he intended it to be.

It is unlikely that French would have much sympathy with Mrs. Cooney's aspirations, but he certainly didn't intend to offend her, for while he could be firm, he disliked hurting people's feelings. Sometimes things might irritate or annoy him, as happens to all of us, but he was a man who seldom openly displayed how he felt. Only once did he ever allow real annoyance to reveal itself in a song. This was when, in retaliation for very poor service received in a hostelry, he wrote "Mick's Hotel" as a genuine indictment since he couldn't get any satisfaction from the owner.

MICK'S HOTEL

NEVER AGAIN FOR ME.

Has anybody ever been to Mick's Hotel,
Mick's Hotel by the salt say water?
None o'yez ha' been there—just as well!
Just as well for ye!—Oh!
If ye were an ostheridge ye might contrive
To get away from the place alive;
They charge you a dollar for a meal you couldn't swaller,
And it's down by the silver sea.
Oh yes, I've been there,
Yes, I was green there,
Hoping that the waiter might perhaps attend to me
"What's in that tureen there?"
"Soup, sir," it's been there
Never again for me.

I went up to the bedroom, but I couldn't find the soap.
"Soap! is it soap by the salt say water?"
I went to ring the bell, but I couldn't find the rope,
And the waiter says to me,
"What the divil do ye want with a bedroom bell,
Haven't you a voice, and can't you yell!"
I made the waiter holler! but it cost me a dollar
Down by the silver sea.
Oh yes, I've been there,
Wits sure are keen there,
But I was in no humour for the lad's jocosity;
Yes, I have been there,
Mick's King and Queen there.
Never again for me.

"Your're waiting for your breakfast, sir, and now what will you
                                take?
Fish! is it fish by the salt say water?
All gone up to Dublin sir, before you were awake."
"Kidneys and toast and tea."
Well now, there was a kidney, but I think it was last week,
Oh, the tea and the toast isn't far to seek,
And marmalade to folla' that'll cost another dollar,
Down by the silver sea.
Oh, I have been there,
Yes, I've been seen there,
Hoping against hope for that second cup of tea.
Oh, yes, I've been there,
Shall I be seen there?
Never again for me.

"You're going in the morning, and you'll want to pay your bill."
Bill! Oh, the bill by the salt say water!
If you want to see the size of it you've got to climb a hill,
Or spread it on the silver sea.
They work by "double entry"—then they multiply by three
And still there's three and sixpence that they haven't got from me.
"Oh, ye washed his flannel collar, put down 'Laundry—one dollar!'
Though you washed it in the silver sea."
Oh yes, I've been there,
Cleaned out quite clean there.
The waiter can't explain the bill, and Mick you never see.
Oh, yes, I've been there,
I got quite lean there,
Never again for me.

    French admitted in after years that the song was written about
a real seaside hotel on the west coast of Ireland, and that "Mick"
had shown himself so indifferent to mild, reasonable and genuine
complaints as to warrant being lampooned; but he would never
reveal where the culprit's hotel was. Many people have guessed

at the location and some places have even claimed the doubtful privilege. Seaside hotels have greatly improved in Ireland over the last quarter-century, so let us hope that although "Mick", whoever he was, is with us no more, he led the way and mended his ways, as well as improving his hospitality.

However "Mick" may have taken it, one other satirical song, which became quite famous, didn't please the victims at all, for they threatened to take action for damages against the great entertainer.

During those days the West Clare Railway ambled on an amiable track along the beautiful coast of Clare from Ennis to Kilkee and Kilrush, stopping at innumerable stations, sometimes to enquire whether John Joe had recovered from the measles, or if Mrs. Murphy's cow had calved yet. Time in the last century didn't matter so much (does it count all that much in Ireland even today?) and the train "might" arrive at a specified hour, or at some more "convainyint" time later on. As trains go, it had a fine, sensible approach to the tedious business of life. It often carried W. P. French with his banjo, box of paints, bicycle and other paraphernalia, for some of his most regular and favourite places of call were situated around or near that very coast—Kilkee, Kilrush, Lisdoonvarna, Ennis; and many is the night when "Moore's Hall in Kilkee was much too small to hold the crowd who wished to hear him. The overflow would keep peering in through the windows".*

One night in Kilkee they peered in vain, for W. P. French didn't arrive. The train had meandered too long on this occasion, and arrived too late for the concert. His reply was a swift one as he echoed the voice of the train guard in a song.

---

*Patricia Lavelle—"James O'Mara—a Staunch Sinn Féiner": Moore's is now The Hydro.

"ARE YE RIGHT THERE, MICHAEL?"

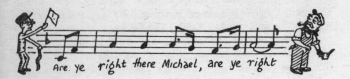

Are ye right there Michael, are ye right

A Lay on the Wild West Clare

1. You may talk of Columbus's sailing
        Across the Atlantical sea
   But he never tried to go railing
        From Ennis as far as Kilkee.
   You run for the train in the mornin',
        The excursion train starting at eight,
   You're there when the clock gives the warnin',
        And there for an hour you'll wait.

(*Spoken*):   And as you're waiting in the train,
        You'll hear the guard sing this refrain:—

   "Are ye right there, Michael? are ye right?
   Do you think that we'll be there before the night?
        Ye've been so long in startin',
        That ye couldn't say for sartin'—
   Still ye might now, Michael, so ye might!"

2. They find out where the engine's been hiding,
        And it drags you to Sweet Corofin;
   Says the guard, "Back her down on the siding
        There's the goods from Kilrush comin' in."
   Perhaps it comes in in two hours,
        Perhaps it breaks down on the way ;
   "If it does," says the guard, "be the powers
        We're here for the rest of the day !"

(*Spoken*):   And while you sit and curse your luck,
              The train backs down into a truck.

              "Are ye right there, Michael? are ye right?
              Have ye got the parcel there for Mrs. White?
                    Ye haven't, Oh, Begorra,
                    Say it's comin' down to-morra—
              And it might now, Michael, so it might"

3. At Lahinch the sea shines like a jewel,
        With joy you are ready to shout,
   When the stoker cries out, "There's no fuel,
        And the fire's taytotally out.
   But hand up that bit of a log there—
        I'll soon have ye out of the fix;
   There's a fine clamp of turf in the bog there;"
        And the rest go a-gatherin' sticks.

(*Spoken*):   And while you're breakin' bits of trees,
              You hear some wise remarks like these:—

              "Are ye right there, Michael? are ye right?
              Do ye think ye can get the fire to light?"
                    "Oh, an hour you'll require,
                    For the turf it might be drier—"
              "Well, it might now, Michael, so it might."

4. Kilkee! Oh, you never get near it!
        You're in luck if the train brings you back,
   For the permanent way is so queer, it
        Spends most of its time off the track,
   Uphill the ould engin' is climbin',
        While the passengers push with a will;
   You're in luck when you reach Ennistymon,
        For all the way home is down-hill.

(*Spoken*): And as you're wobbling through the dark,
            You hear the guard make this remark:—

            "Are ye right there, Michael? are ye right?
            Do you think that ye'll be home before it's light?"
                  "'Tis all dependin' whether
                  The ould engin' howlds together—"
            "And it might now, Michael, so it might!"

"Are ye right there, Michael?" made audiences laugh, but the owners of the railway weren't amused. They took offence and entered an action for libel against the song-writer. French, who treated the whole affair as a huge joke, riposted by entering a counter claim against the railway—for being the cause of keeping him late for a professional engagement.

There might have been some fun in court had the quick-witted entertainer succeeded in appearing in the witness-box; but maybe the company anticipated that, for they backed out at the last moment and made a settlement in his favour. Adding further point to a complicated joke is the story that French completed the correspondence in connection with the case in the house of a gentleman named Glynn with whom he had been staying at Kilrush, not knowing that his host was a shareholder in the company, and that his brother was managing-director. Mr. Glynn is said to have related the story with great gusto in after years to the younger Val Vousden, a fellow entertainer.

The West Clare Railway is now, regrettably, a thing of the past, as it was one of the branch lines eliminated in the recent drastic reconstruction by the country's national transport company. So, the journey commemorated in Percy French's song is only a memory, and cannot be repeated.

French was entirely devoid of malice in the affair, as might be expected of him. He often travelled on that same railway after-wards, and was the best of friends with the original Michael, and his son after him. He came to be regarded as an honoured guest who had established their fame. Today there is a practical sign that the old difference has been forgotten, for the railway company have placed a commemorative plaque at Ennis station from where the famous journey started, and the actual engine, "Bessborough", stands nearby resplendent in a brand-new coat of paint. The original "Michael" is said to have been Michael Talty, for many years head porter at Kilrush, who died at the age of 99 in 1957. His last wish was to live to be 100, as he had been promised a bottle of whisky on reaching the century. His wish, alas, was not fulfilled.

He was a big, strong, man; and was always sent to quell the rioters on the special train to Miltown Malbay races. Another Michael (Donovan), is still driving trains, and was the last driver of the famous West Clare.

In fact, French, who loved the countryside of Clare, looked forward to his summer visits, and in the course of time he gathered many friends in the district. It inspired another of his better-known songs, "The Girl from Clare", with the sister version which he probably wrote for the female companion in his act in later years, May Laffin.

THE DARLIN' GIRL FROM CLARE

WE WERE SITTIN' ON THE WALL UPON A SUNDAY

We were sittin' on the wall upon a Sunday
To watch the girls go by,
And thinkin' we'd be marrit to one one day
When Kate Flynn caught our eye.
Oh, man! she was the makin's of a fairy,
And it made each boyo swear,
"There's not one girl in the wide, wide world
   Like the girl from the County Clare!"

> *Chorus:*
> And ev'ry man had got the finest plan
> You ever see now—barrin' me now,
> Ev'ry day there's one of them would say,
> That she'll agree now—you'll see now;
> All night they'd fight,
> As to which o' them was right,
> In the colour of her eyes and hair,
> But not a word from me was ever heard,
> About the darlin' girl from Clare!

Says Fagin, "'Tis the father I'll be plazin',
I'll tell him of the land I've tilled,
I'll tell him of the cattle I have grazin'
And the house I mean to build;
And whin he sees the 'arable' and 'pasture'
And the fat stock feedin' there,
An' the hens an' the chickens,
Ye may go to the dickens
For the girl from the County Clare."

Chorus:

So every man had got the finest plan
Ye ever see now—barrin' me now,
Ev'ry day there's one of them would say
That she'll agree now—you'll see now
*Thinks I "Well then now
Though I haven't ere a cow
Of brass I've got my share,
And so I know the way they ought to go
About the darlin' girl from Clare."

Sez Sharkey, "She'll be coming to the shop there
To buy some sort of thing,
I'll ax her if she has a mind to stop there,
And should I buy the ring:
An' whin she sees the curtains on the windas,
An' the old clock on the stair
Keepin' time to the minit,
No one else will be in it
With the darlin' girl from Clare!"

Chorus:

So every man had got the finest plan
Ye ever see now—barrin' me now,
Ev'ry day there's one of them would say,
That she'll agree now—you'll see now,
Thinks I "ye may stop
Till yer dead in yer shop,
An' not a hair she'll care,
Wid all yer gold
Ye'll never hold a hold
Upon the darlin' girl from Clare."

*Original lines here were:
        "Thinks I to meself
        Though I haven't got the pelf"

I never said a single word about her,
But I met the girl that day,
I told her I could never live widout her,
An' what had she to say?
She said that I might go and see her father:
I met him then and there,
An' in less than an hour
We were fightin' for the dower
Of the darlin' girl from Clare!

Chorus:

So ev'ry man had got the finest plan
Ye ever see now—barrin' me now,
Ev'ry day there's one of them would say
That she'll agree now—you'll see now;
But late last night
When the moon was bright
I axed her if she'd share
Me joy an' me sorra'—
An' begorra! on tomorra'
I'll be married to the girl from Clare!

DARLIN' GIRL FROM CLARE

(*Ladies' Version*)

I haven't any right to be complaining
Wid three strings to my bow,
I declare to you it's lovers it is raining!
On every bush they grow ;
I'm told they talk about me night and morning,
And every boy will swear,
"There's not a pearl in the wide, wide worl'
Like the girl from the County Clare!"

Chorus:

> And ev'ry man has got the finest plan
> Ye ever see now—'bout me now,
> Ev'ry day there's one of them would say
> That she'll agree now—you will see now;
> All night they'll fight
> As to which had got the right
> My property to share,
> But oh! boys oh!
> That's not the way to go,
> To win the darlin' girl from Clare.

Says Phelim, "'Tis the father I'll be plazin'
I'll tell him of the land I've tilled,
I'll tell him of the cattle I have grazin'
And the house I mean to build;
And whin he sees the 'arable' and 'pasture'
And the fat stock feedin' there,
An' the hens an' the chickens,
Ye may go to the dickens
For the girl from the County Clare."

Chorus

> So ev'ry man had got the finest plan
> Ye ever see now—'bout me now,
> Ev'ry day there's one of them would say
> That she'll agree now—you'll see now;
> Thinks I "You're grand,
> Wid your house and your land,"
> But I'm not wanting there,
> For oh! boys oh!
> That's not the way to go
> About the darlin' girl from Clare."

Sez Connor, "She'll be coming to the shop there
To buy some sort of thing,
I'll ax her if she has a mind to stop there,
And should I buy the ring;
An' whin she sees the curtains on the windas,
An' the old clock on the stair
Keepin' time to the minit,
No one else will be in it
With the darlin' girl from Clare."

Chorus:

So ev'ry man had got the finest plan
Ye ever see now—'bout me now,
Ev'ry day there's one of them would say
That she'll agree now—you'll see now
Thinks I "Ye may stop
Till yer dead in yer shop
An' not a hair I'll care,
Wid all your gold
Ye'll never hold a hold
Upon the darlin' girl from Clare."

But Seamus came and put his arms about me,
Oh! he's the right boy, too,
He told me he could never live without me,
And so what could I do!
I told him he must go and see me father,
He kissed me then and there,
And in less than an hour
He was fighting for the dower
Of the darlin' girl from Clare.

Chorus:

So ev'ry man had got the finest plan
Ye ever see now—'bout me now,
Ev'ry day there's one of them would say
That she'll agree now—you'll see now;

But late last night
When the moon was bright
He axed me if I'd share
His joy an' his sorra'—
An' begorral on to-morra'
He'll be married to the girl from Clare!

In those early days, however, French was quite alone on his travels, and would delight in cycling from one engagement to another when the distances were not too great. By this means he could stop when the inclination came and indulge what was probably his greatest satisfaction when setting up his easel by a rutty road, opening  his box of paints, and capturing the landscape in the delicate shades of his water-colours. His paintings were mainly made with the intention of selling them, (in many places he would have an "art" show during the day) but many were scattered with careless generosity among the friends of his travels —gestures for kindness received, or friendship maintained. Many are now in the hands of the French family.

By using his bicycle he could also meet and talk to the ordinary people who gave him the material for his most inspired songs. In talking to them, and reaching for their hearts there were two things at least in his favour, and these were important; he genuinely loved their company, and he never tried to condescend to them. They accepted Percy French, and so he was able to so faithfully reflect their moods, and capture, as in a miniature, their little affairs.

PHISTLIN' PHIL McHUGH

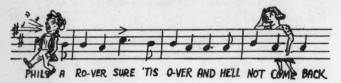

PHIL'S A RO-VER SURE 'TIS O-VER AND HE'LL NOT COME BACK

Oh! Phistlin' Phil McHugh
Has come over from Bunlaghy,
An' I don't know what's come to
Little Mary Ann Mulcahy;
For ever since the day
That Phil he came a-phistlin'
She stands in the doorway,
An' she's waitin' an' she's listnin'.

> *Chorus:*
> Oh, Mary, you're contrary—
> Come in an' shut the door;
> Phil's a rover, sure 'tis over,
> And he'll not come back, asthore.
> But she's listnin' for the phistlin'
> And she's waitin' by the shore,
> For that arrum to be warum
> Round her waist once more.

There's Thady of the Cows—
Sure you know "Ten-acre Thady",
With his fine new slated house,
He'd make her quite the lady.
But Thady needn't stay,
For there's no use his inthragin'
For her heart is far away—
'Tis wid Phil McHugh stravagin'.

Chorus:
Oh, Mary, you're contrary—
Come in an' shut the door;
Phil's a rover, sure 'tis over,
And he'll not come back, asthore.
But she's listnin' for the phistlin'
And she's waitin' by the shore,
For that arrum to be warum
Round her waist once more.

'Tis wisdom's golden rule
I do teach her till I tire,
That every girl's a fool,
Ay, and every man's a liar.
What's that, you say, you hear,
That's set you all a thrimbly,
'Tis but the wind I fear
That is phistlin' down the chimbly.

Chorus:
Oh, Mary, you're contrary—
Come in an' shut the door;
Phil's a rover, sure 'tis over,
And he'll not come back, asthore.
But she's listnin' for the phistlin'
And she's waitin' by the shore,
For that arrum to be warum
Round her waist once more.

There's Danny Michael Dan,
Who is six fut in his stockin's
A very proper man,
But she never heeds his knockin's
She'd keep him standin' there
For three-quarters of a minit,
But she's racin like a hare
When she thinks that Phil is in it.

> *Chorus:*
> Oh, Mary, you're contrary—
> Come in and bar the door;
> What's that scufflin'? Phil, you ruffian;
> Sure I knew he'd come, asthore.
> She's been settin' there and frettin',
> But now her grievin's o'er
> And the singin' will be ringing
> In her heart once more.

In the modern published editions of this song the title name is usually spelt "Whistlin' Phil McHugh", but, for the sound it conveys of a whistle and for the alliterative effect, "Phistlin'" was the word intended by French.

This and other changes of spelling have been made so that the meaning would be clear to eyes and ears unaccustomed to the sound of an Irish accent, but, while understandable, this seems to be contrariwise to French's intention which was to record the sounds, phonetically, as they came to him; and he undoubtedly intended anyone singing them to do the same thing. His original spelling has therefore been used throughout this book.

The spelling of words in this way was a reason, sometimes, for a suggestion of "stage-Irish" since people felt they were being "made game of"—succumbing to an inherent belief in those days that possession of a distinctive "Irish" accent was in some sense admitting inferiority, and that to mimic it was in its own way a national insult. Nowadays Irish people have more pride and contentment in their own characteristics, and therefore less desire to ape the vocal tones of "The Strangers," so there is less possibility of offence.

The Irish way of speaking varies very much from North to South. French's effort to portray the different tones, with no more than very occasional slips in phrasing, is very near the mark. In his recitation "The Four Farrellys", for instance, he not only set down accents for four quarters of the country—Belfast, Dublin, Kerry and Mayo, but showed a practical knowledge of them when performing this number on the stage. A careful examination of, say, Phil the Fluther will reveal subtle differences in phrase as against "Phistlin' Phil", as the first Phil inhabited the North (Cavan/Leitrim) while the other Phil's wanderings were in the West. In "Mat Hannigan's Aunt" there are hints of the accent of Dublin, for there the song was written.

The clarification of certain words as used in " Phistlin' Phil" may help in easing the way in other lyrics.

Asthore—from the Gaelic "A Stór"—(my) treasure.
arrum—arm: in the South and West we say it like this.
warum, equally—warm.
slated house—most houses in the West were, and often still
        are, thatched. The possession of a "slated"
        house would be quite a matter of prestige
        half-a-century ago.
inthragin'—intriguing,=scheming
stravagin'—stravaging,=wandering
thrimbly—trembly,=trembling
chimbly—chimney. Most country people say, or did say,
      chimbley.

Danny Michael Dan—In the South-West and West in
                  particular several Christian names are
                  often used to distinguish one member
                  of a family from his relations. It is a
                  custom to hand family names down.
                  Quite frequently the father's name will
                  be used second, and the Grandfather's
                  third, and this will set the man's
                  immediate family history for anyone
                  referring to him in the district. This
                  man's brother, for instance, might be
                  Billy Michael Dan. It is a system
                  which has its use in certain areas
                  where through the survival of the old
                  clan members, many people have the
                  same surnames. Irish surnames were
                  developed basically in this way in the
                  first instance: i.e. O'Donnell means
                  "son of Donal".

As Percy French himself said "an aristocrat is always at home in Connemara" for these apparently simple, shrewd men of the West, who have a natural dignity and reserve, allied to kindliness, and are gentlemen by nature, are not long in detecting a poseur.

Vousden told some wonderful stories of Percy French's travels in the West. Perhaps they cannot all be entirely relied on since Vousden's account of his fellow Thespian while warm, generous and beautifully shaded in character is coloured with a little imagination. It was hardly correct, for instance, to suggest that French might or might not be expected to turn up for an engagement "He might take the wrong train or go somewhere else". The only occasion which has been recorded of a concert being missed was when the train was late at Kilkee—and he thought this so unusual as to perpetuate it in a song. Nevertheless, behind Vousden's stories lies a warm admiration for the older man. These are his words: "One beautiful September day, when little waves were making music against the trawlers alongside the wooden pier, he was in great form with his natural friends, the big men who go down to the sea in ships. Said one of them, ''Tis the wondher o' the world, sir, that ye wouldn't go on the stage; 'tis a power o' money you'd be gettin' '. When Percy moved away one of the more initiated said: 'Yerra, Meehaul, why did you say that? Sure isn't he the clown that does be playin' the banjo at the concerts'."

He recorded that another day when French had finished a day's painting he called into a wayside pub, paintings under the arm, and treated the locals who were there with hilarious stories and liquid refreshment. As he left one of the "victims", wiping the tears of laughter from his eyes remarked "Be the mortal man, 'tis an awful mistake for a man like that to be wastin' his time hawkin' that stuff around, whatever the devil it is, for he'd make a fortune if he went on the stage." He wasn't to know that French was on his way to a hard night's work on the boards.

These stories sound very like some of those W. P. French would half-acquire and half-invent and tell against himself, with his tongue firmly in his cheek—so he has only himself to blame if, in the memory of a fellow-entertainer, they have wrongly mirrored his character! For all their possible invention they do give a real picture of the sturdy little figure which could be encountered

many a day on a bogland road half-a-century ago with paints and
easel and far-seeing eyes.

One day, while resting on a fine summers afternoon on the cliffs
of Skerries, above Dublin, those eyes saw the "Mountains of
Mourne sweeping down to the sea" on the far Coast of Ulster
and Percy French's most famous song was born.

THE MOUNTAINS OF MOURNE

Oh, Mary, this London's a wonderful sight,
Wid the people here workin' by day and by night:
They don't sow potatoes, nor barley, nor wheat,
But there's gangs o' them diggin' for gold in the street—
At least, when I axed them, that's what I was told:
So I just took a hand at this diggin' for gold.
But for all that I found there, I might as well be
Where the Mountains o' Mourne sweep down to the sea.

I believe that, when writin', a wish you expressed
As to how the fine ladies in London were dressed.
Well, if you'll believe me, when axed to a ball,
They don't wear a top to their dresses at all!
Oh, I've seen them meself, and you could not, in thrath,
Say, if they were bound for a ball or a bath—
Don't be startin' them fashions now, Mary Machree,
Where the Mountains o' Mourne sweep down to the sea.

I seen England's King from the top of a 'bus—
I never knew him, though he means to know us:
And though by the Saxon we once were oppressed,
Still, I cheered—God forgive me—I cheered wid the rest.
And now that he's visited Erin's green shore,
We'll be much better friends than we've been heretofore
When we've got all we want, we're quiet as can be
Where the Mountains o' Mourne sweep down to the sea.

You remember young Peter O'Loughlin, of course—
Well, here he is now at the head o' the Force.
I met him to-day, I was crossin' the Strand,
And he stopped the whole street wid wan wave of his hand.
And there we stood talking of days that are gone
While the whole population of London looked on;
But for all these great powers, he's wishful like me,
To be back where dark Mourne sweeps down to the sea.

There's beautiful girls here—oh, never mind!—
With beautiful shapes Nature never designed,
And lovely complexions, all roses and crame
But O'Loughlin remarked wid regard to them same:
"That if at those roses you venture to sip,
The colour might all come away on your lip,"
So I'll wait for the wild rose that's waitin' for me—
Where the Mountains of Mourne sweep down to the sea.

The verses, penned on the back of a postcard, were despatched to Houston Collisson, and he set it to the same plaintive traditional air which Denny Lane used for "Carrighdoun"; but, by a process which could be most simply described as "doubling up on the notes" Collisson cleverly transformed the tune so that, to a casual ear, it sounds quite different.

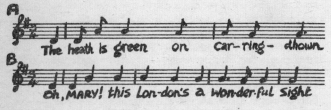

(*Musical examples of both*)

There is a monument standing to-day, under the shadow of the Mourne Mountains, at Newcastle, Co. Down to Percy French and his song. It is odd to reflect that when his publishers, Pigotts, first received the song, they turned it down as "not serious enough for a ballad, not funny enough for a comic-song." One of Pigotts readers persuaded them to take it, and it made plenty of money for them both, establishing French as a song-writer, and giving the entree to engagements in England. It has been imitated and parodied many times, but no version has been as successful as the original. Imitations seldom have the impact of a good original, but another reason in this case is that despite the apparent stage-Irish comedy of the lyric there is an underlying pathos and sincerity which makes the song good for more than a laugh. The tune and the sentiment are sympathetic. French understood and had feelings for the lone Irish boy in the strange world of London. He was a country boy himself at heart, and would feel homesick many a day during his future years in the "big city".

The sympathy of feeling which existed in collaboration between Collisson and French cannot be seen more plainly than in this song, where music and words are perfectly in tune with each other: but, although close friends they never got beyond surnames and when addressing each other, it was always "French" and, "Collisson" in the best public-school manner.

In the following years the little doctor was to provide much of the music when new tunes were required, but times were changing for him, as they were to change for Percy French.

Collisson, a doctor of music since 1890, had been studying arts at Trinity, and graduated in 1897. He then left for Kildare to commence study for Holy Orders; became a clergyman two years later, and left Ireland to spend the first few years of his calling in Cornwall.

Unlike French, who refrained from making public such views as he might have, Collisson had very strong opinions on the most dangerous subjects of controversy in Ireland—religion and politics, and he didn't hesitate to express them. His ideas were often in advance of those of his times.

The undercurrent of national feeling was gaining a fresh impetus in Ireland near the turn of the century. Thought of action was confined to small minority groups, with no indication of the upheaval which would change the whole political structure of the country within the coming twenty-five years; but the Gaelic League, founded in 1893, had, by an emphasis on things Irish in literature and culture, made a large number of the people in the country nation-proud, who before had been indifferent.

Collisson was, to some extent, affected by this feeling. While not active politically, he favoured the national side, and in regard to religion, his view point was most tolerant. Nevertheless, he was once or twice badly received, and even roughly handled, while carrying out his own solo entertainment because some of the nationally-minded majority thought that since he possessed a Trinity accent and a Protestant clergyman's garb he would be "agin" them.

In Birr, for instance, on one occasion in 1906, part of the audience, in a demonstration which might have been prearranged, showed some disapproval, and a local newspaper next day picked particularly on the Percy French song "Wait for a while now, Mary" suggesting that it was making a mock of national sentiment by laughing at it. This was not so—French never laughed *at* the people; he laughed *with* them which is quite a different thing, and probably understood them a good deal better than the person who criticised his song. Nevertheless, this was the kind of criticism sometimes made in the edgy atmosphere of the time, when people of both sides were a little more sensitive in ordinary things, than they might be to-day, so that performers like French or Collisson, although non-political, were sometimes faced with people of two widely varying opinions, and made the victims of one or the other.

The fact that the better dressed part of the audience, or "Shoneens" as the critical newspaper called them, were bent on showing approval probably didn't help Collisson at all on this occasion, but added to the "divilment". The song itself is innocent enough, and nowadays it would be hard to see where the offence might lie.

WAIT FOR A WHILE NOW MARY

I had plenty to do
And was only half through,
And the bats were beginning to wheel;
When who should pass by
On the road from Athy
But sweet little Mary O'Neill,
Without collar or coat,
Like a mountainy goat,
I stood with my face going red.
She had bid me good-day,
And was turning away,
When all in a fluster I said:—

> *Chorus:*
> "Wait for a while now Mary,
> I've something more to say;
> Wait for a while now, Mary,
> You needn't run away"
> "Oh, it's all very fine," says Mary,
> "I can't stay here all day."
> Says I, "Don't fret,
> 'Tis early yet"
> That's all I found to say.

Says I, "By-the-bye,
Did you hear in Athy
What Hennessy got for his cow?"
Says she, "Do you know
That you haven't let go
Of my hand since you took it just now?"
"Well I can't understand
What came over my hand
To be squeezing your fingers like that."
Says she, "I must go
It's not proper, you know!"
But I said as she straightened her hat.

Chorus:

"Wait for a while now, Mary,
I've something more to say;
Wait for a while now, Mary,
You needn't run away".
"Oh, it's all very fine," says Mary,
"I'm wasting all my day."
Says I, "That's true—
I'll waste mine too"
That's all I found to say.

Says I "There's a mare
In the meadow down there
Worth forty—I wouldn't take less."
Says she, in some haste:
"Oh, your arm's round my waist
And it's spoiling the sit of my dress!"
"Now, how in the world
My arm got curled—
I'll try to explain to you Miss."
Says she, "Don't explain,
For it's perfectly plain
I'd better be home out of this!"

Chorus:

"Wait for a while now, Mary
I know what I've to say;
Wait for a while now, Mary
You've stole my heart away!"
"Did it not meet mine?" says Mary
"It passed yours on the way!"
*"Oh tabhair 'm póg
Ma Colleen óg!"
That's all I found to say.

*"O, Give me a kiss, my little young girl"

It was almost inevitable, that such incidents should occur when religion was being so closely associated with the wish for national independence, but they greatly distressed the kindly little man, who hated to be called, or regarded as, a "West Briton." In fact, some of his most valued friends around the country were Catholic priests and it was as a tribute to one of them that he asked Percy French for some verses to set to music, and this resulted in "Father O'Callaghan", a piece reminiscent of Graves's "Father O'Flynn" but with a style of its own.

FATHER O'CALLAGHAN

Father Cornelius O'Callaghan,
　　To most of us Father Con—
To all of us quite the kindliest man,
　　That ever the sun shone on.
I mind me when I was a bit of a lad,
　　He stood with me out in the cold
While I told him of a curious dream I'd had,
　　Of findin' a crock of gold.

"O Father O'Callaghan,
　　When will the dream come true?
O Father O'Callaghan,
　　If anyone knows 'tis you!"
And Father O'Callaghan sthrok'd me pate,
　　Sez he, "The story is old—
Every one that can work and wait
　　Will find his crock of gold."

Rosie Mulvany was bright as a bird,
　　I lov'd her, she didn't object,
But somehow I never could bring out the word,
　　That Rose had a right to expect.

I'd dream of her nightly, I'd dream she said "Yes",
    Be daylight me courage was gone,
I was wore to a shadow, so in my distress,
    I went and I saw Father Con,

"O Father O'Callaghan,
    Will the dream come true?
O Father O'Callaghan,
    What is a boy to do?"
And Father O'Callaghan said, "See here,
    You must call in your Sunday clothes,
Say to her this, 'Will you marry me dear?'
    You can leave the rest to Rose".

We talk'd one night of the glorious days,
    When Ireland led the van,
With scholars as thick as the stars in the sky
    And work for every man.
"'Twill come again," said Father Con,
    And his fertile fancy paints
The glorious day when the sun shines on
    A new Isle of the Saints.

"O Father O'Callaghan,
    When will the dream come true?
O Father O'Callaghan,
    If anyone knows, 'tis you!"
And Father O'Callaghan raised his head,
    And smil'd his humoursome smile,
"When ev'ry man learns to rule himself
    'Twill then be a saintly Isle."

Father O'Callaghan's dead and gone,
    This many and many a day—
But we haven't forgot you Father Con,
    And it keeps us from goin' astray.

And so at the last great earthquake shock,
  When the trumpet's soundin' clear,
He'll guide to their God the faithful flock,
  That knew him and lov'd him here.

"O Father O'Callaghan,
  When will the dream come true?
O Father O'Callaghan,
  If anyone knows 'tis you!"
And Father O'Callaghan says no word,
  For he's sleepin' softly yet,
And when the Archangel's voice is heard,
  We know that he won't forget.

Collisson's feeling for the nationalist viewpoint led him to
suggest that French would write the lyric for "When Erin Wakes"
which, set to music by Collisson, won the award in 1900 at the
Feis Ceoil for the best arrangement of an Irish melody.

The Feis Ceoil, literally meaning "Festival of Music", is
now held in Dublin each Spring, with competitions in singing,
composition and playing of music, mainly with a national flavour.
Dr. Annie Patterson, whose idea it was to revive the Feis Ceoil,
had been associated with Collisson in several musical works
during the previous eight years. "When Erin Wakes" is based on
a fine, stirring air called "The Flight of the Earls", which had
also been used for the well-known "Boys of Wexford." The
sentiments expressed in it are straightforwardly national, yet
the passing of three years brought a song from the same collaboration, on the visit of King Edward to Ireland. It is a conventional
song of welcome, following two cautiously satirical verses; but,
reading closely into it, if one has to do that, it does no more
than say "we welcome the new King, in the hopes that he'll make
things better for Ireland", and that was the hope of the many
ordinary people at the time who came out and cheered the royal
procession.

WHEN ERIN WAKES

Air: "The Flight of the Earls"

Let newer nations fill the stage,
And vaunt them to the sky:
The Gael has still a heritage
That gold can never buy;
The mountains may be bleak and bare,
Forlorn the country side,
But great Cuchulainn battled there
And "Red Branch" heroes died.
And as of old, our headlands bold
Still front the raging sea,
So may our band united stand,
As fearless and as free.

I hear the lays of other days
In martial numbers flow,
King Death's the only sword that stays
The march of Owen Roe.
At Fontenoy the breezes bore
The war cry of the Gael,
And Saxon standards fled before
The sons of Innisfail.
And as of old our headlands bold
Still front the raging sea,
So may our band united stand
As fearless and as free.

Beneath the rath the heroes sleep,
Their steeds beside them stand,
Each falchion from its sheath shall leap
To guard old Ireland:
The legend we may yet fulfil
And play the heroes part
For Sarsfield's spirit slumbers still
In many an Irish heart

And as of old our headlands bold
Still front the raging sea,
So may our band united stand
As fearless and as free.

KING EDWARD IN ERIN

'Twas late in the evening as home I did go
To sweet Crossmolina in County Mayo,
I met an old harper who play'd on wan string,
And the tune he was playin' was "God save the King!"

> *Chorus:*
> "God save the King!"
> He made the rocks ring
> Wid de way he was weltin' out
> "God save the King!"

Says I, "Where's the tunes that wor' once in your pate?
Give us 'Erin remember' or try 'Ninety-eight'."
Says he, "It is strange how they're all taken wing
Not a wan I remember but "God save the King!"

> *Chorus:*
> "God save the King!"
> Not a taste of a thing,
> Could the ould man remember
> But "God save the King!"

Says he, there's a change comin' over the land
That an old man like me cannot well understand
Wid Redmond and Saunderson all in wan ring
And footin' it nately to "God save the King!"

> *Chorus:*
> "God save the King!"
> Together we'll cling,
> All crackin' their voices wid
> "God save the King!"

I mind well the day when the league of the Gael,
Would have scowled at the sight of the Sassenach sail
But now the King's yacht at her moorings may swing
Wid the Britain St. band playing "God save the King!"

> *Chorus:*
> "God save the King!"
> Its a wonderful thing
> To see Capel Street marchin' to
> "God save the King!"

For the King that's come over to see us at last,
Has nothin' to do wid the days that are past
And though there are some that to sorrows will cling,
For a while we'll forget them and welcome the King.

> *Chorus:*
> "God save the King!"
> For his reign seems to bring
> A respite to Erin, so
> God save the King!

Those sympathetic to Dublin Castle might raise a polite eyebrow
at the sentiments of "When Erin Wakes"; just as the thought of
welcoming Edward would make a nationalist, believing that no
English King had the right to rule in Ireland, scowl. Being somewhere in between it is unlikely that French saw anything in-
congruous in producing either of the lyrics. He loved Ireland:
and was also quite prepared to welcome King Edward. It merely
emphasises the point made by his cousin, although to say that
French had no interest in politics is not to say that he had no
interest in Ireland. But, he was not at his best when dealing with
such songs for specific occasions, and it is a relief to find another
song written in the same year as the Feis Ceoil winner, partly
to the Irish Washerwoman Jig, which has no political implications
at all, and is therefore more in his true form.

McBREEN'S HEIFER

WHETHER THERE'S THE DIFFER OF THE PRICE—HEIFER

McBreen had two daughters, and each one in turn
Was offered in marriage to Jamesy O'Byrne:
Now Kitty was pretty, but Jane she was plain
So, to make up the differ, McBreen would explain
He'd give the best heifer he had on the land,
As a sort of a bonus, with Jane, understand—
But then Kitty would charm a bird off a bush
And that left the lad in a horrid non-plush.

Chorus:

Now there's no denyin' Kitty was remarkably pretty,
Tho' I can't say the same for Jane,
But still there's not the differ of the price of a heifer,
Between the pretty and the plain.

Entirely bother'd was Jamesy O'Byrne
He thought that he'd give the school-master a turn;
Sez he "To wed Kitty is very good fun,
Still a heifer's a heifer when all's said an' done.
A girl she might lose her good looks any how—
And a heifer might grow to an elegant cow;
But still there's no price for the stock, d'ye mind.
And Jane has a face that the Divil designed."

Chorus:
Now there's no denyin' Kitty was remarkably pretty,
Tho' I can't say the same for Jane,
But still there's not the differ of the price of a heifer,
Between the pretty and the plain.

The school-master said, with a good deal of since,
We'll reduce the two girls to shillin's an' pence,
Add the price of the heifer when Jane I'll be bound
Will come out the top by a couple o' pound.
But still I'm forgettin' that down in Glengall
The stock is just goin' for nothin' at all;
So Jim thought he'd wait till the end of the year.
Till girls might be cheaper or stock might be dear.

Chorus:
But when he came for Kitty, she was married to McVittie.
And McBlane had appropriated Jane,
So whether there's the differ of the price of a heifer,
Is a thing that he never could explain.

Once a porter in a hotel asked him, in apparent seriousness "Did ye get rid o' that heifer yet, sir?" One imagines that the porter had his tongue to his cheek and that Percy French had pulled too many legs in his time to be caught by that one.

Because there was a real Phil the Fluther, or an original Paddy Reilly, there may be a tendency to think that every song ever written by Percy French is about some circumstance or person, whereas many of the later songs, in particular, came about merely as additions to a professional entertainer's repertoire as the necessity of a new season of concerts demanded. Nothing can ever be written, of course, without an idea, and the idea may be conjured up entirely out of the mind, but that is usually less than likely and many scraps of conversation heard on the headlands of Clare, or from the mouth of a character in the bogs "Below Belmullet in the County of Mayo", were probably unconsciously stored in the recesses of Percy French's mind and used to form and colour songs years after. The days when a song might be written as a private joke for the closed circle of a tennis party, or about someone known to all the hearers had passed, however, for now French was to embark in real earnest on a professional stage career, and the old haphazard days were gone for ever.

He had been getting occasional engagements in England, so, aware of the necessity of catering for a growing family, he decided to try his luck in London, the centre of theatrical life. At a time when he was approaching a half-century in years Percy French packed his bags, left the green fields of Ireland behind, and entered the most ruthless and competitive business in the world. Percy French came to town and "The Mountains of Mourne", "Phil the Fluther" and other songs, old and new, became known in a widening circle as the French/Collisson recitals at the Steinway Hall near Portman Square became accepted and recognised as a feature of the theatrical scene.

Percy and Helen French were by now the parents of two daughters, Molly and Ettie, and before long there would be another addition to the growing family. They tried several addresses before settling in at 27 Clifton Hill, N.W., and the father of the family began a busy life, involving himself in journalistic work and serious painting in addition to song writing and a growing list of concert engagements. These latter involved him in a considerable amount of travelling, and his wife, a placid, but firm and shrewd lady, proved just the person for him in seeing that he went to the right place, and on the right date. For years she kept a diary in which all his forward dates were recorded, with the agreed fees, and notes of any special arrangements. The cryptic "E.P." entered against the dates of charitable or other free performances meant more lucrative "Engagements Permitting" (there would have been many more than he could afford had it been left entirely to the amiable entertainer's discretion.)

He worked with other partners in London apart from Collisson; Harrison Hill, the tenor, being one of the first, but on his travels up and down the country, at least to the end of the Edwardian era, he usually performed alone.

Giving a performance solo, with
nothing to aid you but your own talent,
for two hours or more, is a tremendous
test of the performer's ability and
personality. Even such a calm person as
Percy French would eventually find the
effort of catching and holding an
audience, night after night, a big strain
on his nerves. A lot of the strain can be
reduced, of course, by timing the material
when repetition has made it familiar; but
in fact this is one of the pitfalls the
performer must guard himself against—
making the entertainment too automatic, and therefore lacking in
warmth of expression. That kind of glib performance can be
effective for ten minutes, but not for two hours. The great thing
about Percy French was that his work always seemed to be
spontaneous: as if he had just thought of it. The strain was there,
nevertheless, but, although he often came home very tired,
particularly as the years went by, his family never knew
him to complain, or be otherwise than his calm, kind
self.

Yet, although he was now inescapably in the thick of show
business, and would remain in it, he mixed very little with people
of the stage, and somehow persuaded himself, with an inverted
sense of reasoning, that he was never really in the business at all;
and continued to regard writing and painting as his true vocations.
There was probably an unconscious, but inherited element of
the country gentleman about his attitude, as suggested by his
cousin: "Other qualities of his kind were there also—an easy
mastery of sport, an extraordinary carelessness of appearance
that led him to appear in the most eccentric garb; a complete
inability to look after money. He could make it, he could give it
away, he could—and often did—forget to ask for it, he could
return it because he thought it was too much, he could, with an
infantile cunning, which he regarded as miser-like efficiency, hide
it away so carefully that it was never to be found again. But he
could not keep it. Yet the incapacity for practical affairs, and lack

of scholastic ability on which he prided himself were in large degree a romantic illusion . . ."

The amiable Mr. French could quietly call on the spirit of his ancestors when needed, and administer a devastating snub. Once he was summoned to the London house of a well-known family to make an after-dinner drawing-room appearance for a large fee. On arrival he was instructed to wait in the hall until his services were required. Instead he found his way to the down-stairs quarters, from where, in a short time, sustained sounds of merriment were heard. Presently a message was sent that he could now come and give his performance. Mr. French presented his compliments and regretted that he had already given it—in the kitchen.

Meanwhile the Steinway Hall appearances grew in strength, being now run in conjunction with painting exhibitions at the New Dudley Gallery, 169 Piccadilly, and the songs continued to come out at regular intervals—usually for the London season.

DONEGAN'S DAUGHTER

When Donegan came from the States
Himself and his daughter were seen
Parading the principal streets
Of beautiful Ballyporeen.
Her cheeks were as red as a rose,
Her hair was a beautiful brown,
And the lads, I suppose,
Were as thick now as crows,
All tied to the heel of her gown.

> *Chorus:*
> There were short men and long men,
> And weak men and strong men;
> And right men and wrong men
> Were all to be seen:
> But Donegan's daughter
> From over the water,
> She gave them no quarter
> In Ballyporeen.

She sang the most beautiful songs—
Of the words we had never a hint,
For her fingers went hammer and tongs
In a running accompaniment.
Like a dog running after a rat,
Such scrimmaging never was heard.
Then down went her claws, like a murdering cat
When it leps on the back of a bird.

> *Chorus:*
> At every party
> She sang them all forte
> From "Ah Che la morte"
> To "Wearin' the Green".
> Oh! Donegan's daughter,
> From over the water,
> 'Twas little they taught her
> In Ballyporeen.

The Geraghtys gave a grand ball,
The girls were all ribbons and tape
But Miss Donegan bested them all
With her perfectly wonderful shape;
And when she was taking the floor
With a high-stepping bachelor boy,
The rest of us scowled
In the doorway and growled
That 'twas him we would surely destroy.

> *Chorus:*
> There was kissing and squeezing
> And coaxing and teasing
> And sure there's no reason
> Such things should be seen.
> But Donegan's daughter
> From over the water,
> 'Twas she made the slaughter
> In Ballyporeen.

Coming home we were crossing a stream:
I thought to beleaguer the belle;
A struggle, a kiss, and a scream
And into the water we fell.
To me that can swim like a trout
It was only a trifling reverse:
But when she came out,
'Faith there wasn't much doubt
She was changed very much for the worse.

Chorus:
For her roses had wilted,
Her wig it was tilted,
The figure she'd built, it
Was washed away clean:
Oh! Donegan's daughter
From under the water,
Two pins would have bought her
In Ballyporeen.

MRS. BRADY

Ould Brady's gone to glory, and the widda has the land,
And as she's good to look at, you can easy understand
That eligible suitors from the town of Athenry
Put on their best embellishments, and thought they'd have a try
Jim Flynn, the stationmaster's son, though not in Brady's set,
Was kind enough to say to her, one evening when they met:

Chorus:
"Mrs. Brady, just a whisper!
To your mourning bid adieu!
I know a fine young gentleman
Who'd not object to you.
My family may cut me,
But you've brass enough for two."
"I know who has the brass," says Mrs. Brady.
"Brass enough for three," says Mrs. Brady.

Pat Dempsey heard that Jimmy had been sent against the wall;
Says Pat, "It's not gentility the widda wants at all.
But 'pity is akin to love,' as everybody knows.
I'll tell her how I've got no girl to wash or mend my clothes."
He dressed up like a scarecrow that across a field was hung,
And this was the come-hither that came slipping off his tongue.

Chorus:

"Mrs. Brady, just a whisper!
I'd be glad to marry you
For indeed I've none to help me
With the work I have to do;
And the victuals that they cook me
I can neither chop nor chew."
"I would not suit the place," says Mrs. Brady.
"I'd never do the work," says Mrs. Brady.

Then little Francis Fogarty said, "Women, old and young,
Have always been deluthered by the civil-spoken tongue;
I'll tell her that her cheeks are like the summer rose in bloom,
Her eyes are like two diamonds, and her breath is sweet perfume,'
So off he goes to call on her, all flattery and lies,
And this was how he started in to carry off his prize,

Chorus:

"Mrs. Brady, just a whisper!
There is none as fair as you,
Your face is like the dawn o' day,
Your lips are honey dew;
I'm certain you're an angel,
And it is from heaven you flew."
"I believe you're off your head," says Mrs. Brady
"You ought to see the vet," says Mrs. Brady.

When Flynn, who keeps the grocer's shop, and owns a bit o' land,
Came home and heard how Pat had got the back of Mary's hand,
Says he, "Myself and Mary has been friends through thick and
      thin"
So he put on all his Sunday clothes, and barbarised his chin;
He called on her that morning, she was very sweet and kind.
And this was how he hinted at the thoughts were in his mind:

Chorus:

"Mrs. Brady, just a whisper!
Sure I don't know how to woo;
But I've got a growin' business,
And I've love enough for two;
To name the happy day,
And would to-morrow mornin' do?"
"Why not this afternoon?" says Mrs. Brady.
"There's danger in delay!" says Mrs. Brady.

Mrs. Brady is a number which Collisson sang very well; not so
well known now, perhaps, as some other Percy French songs, it is
nevertheless one of his very best. It was written for the London
concert season, and used by Collisson on his solo Irish tour.

It was when he went to London that he finally became "Percy
French" on the advice of his agent, who felt it had a more straightforward appeal as a stage name than "W. P. French" or "W.
Percy French" as he had been known. His manager at that time
was quite a character, H. S. Franklin, who usually travelled with,
or ahead of, the entertainer making all the business arrangements,
and so relieving French of something he detested having to do.
He always, however, insisted on looking after the lighting himself,
so that his easel and pictures would receive their proper degree
of illumination. Harry Franklin was a Sligo man, and took a lively
part in the musical life of that town, particularly in the organisation
of the local Feis. He played the violin well and while with French
regularly contributed solos as a part of the programme.

In 1906 Collisson had a nervous breakdown, temporarily gave up active participation in the affairs of St. Mary's Church, Seymour Street, and was given leave to undertake a concert tour of Ireland, as a form of rest cure. On returning to London  he set about completing the music, helped by J. A. Robertson, for the children's play "Noah's Ark" which Percy French had written. It went on at the Waldorf Theatre in London that Christmas. The script has not survived, but one of the numbers written for it, "The Hoodoo" remained a concert item of the French/Collisson partnership for several years. It was the second of such plays written by French out of his love for children, the other being *"Freda and the Fairies", a delightful little miniature musical comedy, done with assistance from Cicely Fox-Smith, and with music by Caroline Maude (Countess Hawarden).

These were part of several experiments in writing other than straightforward songs around this time—as witness *"The Kerry Courting", a comedy song-cycle of matchmaking in Ireland, written in 1909, together with a new item for performance by Collisson at the recitals that year—"Bad Ballads for Baddish Babies"

BAD BALLADS FOR BADISH BABIES

No. 1 THE TACTFULLY PATERNAL

> Little Bill, he made an aeroplane, off to France he flew;
> But an upper current caught him and our Bill is over due;
> His Pa from Dover telegraph'd to Ma (at Campden Hill)
> (this gilded pill)
>
> Don't worry dear!
> An over draught
> Just met our little Bill.

*See appendices

No. 2   THE INFANTILE TYRANNICAL
          Edwin and Angela are twins,
          And often kick each other's shins,
          But haven't hurt each other yet
          Their boots are made of flannel-ette!
          They try to pull each other's hair,
          But soon desist in sheer despair,
          For hair is very hard to pull
          When hands are cased in Berlin wool.

No. 3. THE FRANKLY HOMOCIDAL
          The Parents of the Tompkins kid
          Were taught to do as they were bid
          And as the kid was fond of strife
          They led a somewhat harrass'd life.

          One day he order'd them to die,
          They did so almost instantly;
          For in the river's gentle breast
          They found a greatly needed rest.

          One morning, to the kid's despair,
          He found them
          Mr. and Mrs. Tompkins
          "Wrong side up with care!"

No. 4   THE ABSOLUTELY UNANSWERABLE
          Jocasta Jinks had one reply
          To ev'rything; and that was "Why?"
          Her parents were extremely poor
          In ev'rything, except in children to be sure.

          They had a dozen girls and boys
          Who wanted food and clothes and toys
          One day her father whisper'd "Come and see
          What Heaven has sent to you and me."
          Jocasta gazed with look intent
          Upon the babe that Heav'n had sent
          And when Jocasta murmur'd—"Why?"
          Her Pa and Ma made no reply.

After a caricature by Phil May

The recitals at Christmas of 1909 at the Steinway Hall were particularly successful, resulting in approaches for an American engagement from J. C. Duff, the impresario. So in the Autumn of 1910 after a celebration farewell dinner at the Savage Club (to which French had been introduced shortly after taking up residence in London) the two little men, French and Collisson, crossed the Atlantic—a journey foreshadowed for French, but in different circumstances, thirty years before.

On the way the steamer called at Cobh to take on board emigrants bound for America, and a chance remark from one of them gave Percy French the idea for a song in a gently pathetic mood.

Some friends had come to see a fresh-faced young fellow off, and, as the blowing of the tender meant they had to leave him, he looked wistfully at the golden and green fields around the beautiful harbour of Cork and said softly: "You'll be cutting the corn in Creeshla the day".

It was September, and the harvest was coming in.

THE EMIGRANT'S LETTER

DEAR DANNY,

I'm takin' the pen in me hand
To tell you we're just out o' sight o' the land;
In the grand Allen liner we're sailin' in style.
But we're sailin' away from the Emerald Isle;
And a long sort o' sigh seemed to rise from us all
As the waves hid the last bit of ould Donegal.
Och! it's well to be you that is takin' yer tay
Where they're cuttin' the corn in Creeshla the day.

I spoke to the captain—he won't turn her round,
And if I swum back I'd be apt to be drowned,
I'll stay where I am, for the diet is great
The best of combustibles piled on me plate
But though it is "sumpchus", I'd swop the whole lot,
For the ould wooden spoon and the stirabout pot,
And Kitty foreninst me a-wettin' the tay
Where they're cuttin' the corn in Creeshla the day!

There's a woman on board who knows Katey by sight
So we talked of old times 'till they put out the light
I'm to meet the good woman tomorra' on deck
And we'll talk about Katey from this to Quebec.
I know I'm no match for her—oh! not the leesht,
With her house and two cows, and her brother a preesht
But the woman declares Katey's heart's on the say
And mine's back with Katey in Creeshla the day.

If Katey is courted by Patsey or Mick,
Put a word in for me with a lump of a stick,
Don't kill Patsey outright, he had no sort of chance,
But Mickey's a rogue you might murther at wance;
For Katey might think, as the longer she waits,
A boy in the hand is worth two in the States:
And she'll promise to honour, to love and obey
Some robber that's roamin' round Creeshla the day.

Goodbye to you Dan, there's no more to be said,
And I think the salt wather's got into me head,
For it dreeps from me eyes when I call to me mind,
The friends and the Colleen I'm leavin' behind:
But still she might wait; whin I bid her goodbye,
There was just the last taste of a tear in her eye,
And a break in her voice whin she said "You might stay,
But plaze God you'll come back to ould Creeshla some day".

This song was gathered from a real experience—contrast the
genuine feeling in the lyric with the rather trite sympathy of an
earlier song written from a reflex emotion rather than from
something genuine.

THE EMIGRANT SHIP

Bright is the sun above me that is shining
High are the hopes of those who round me press
Why in my heart alone this vain repining?
Why on my cheek the tear of bitterness?
Ah! they are young, and when they feel a yearning
They may perchance recross the angry foam.
But to the old, what hope of e'er returning
Back to the land, where stood their father's home
Ah! Far, far away, where ever we may roam
Far from the land where stood our father's home
Fondly we gaze across the troubled wave, to Ireland, once more.

Room, room for all in the land where we are going,
Bread and to spare, our little ones to feed
No fear of want, to set dissension growing,
No fear the crops will fail us in our need
Still whilst around me youthful hearts are sleeping,
Back o'er the wave, my spirit seems to roam
Once more I see the Shannon by me sweeping,
And the blue mountains of my father's home.
Ah! Far, far away where ever we may roam,
Far from the land where stood our father's home,
Sadly we gaze across the troubled wave, to Ireland once more.

Like many natural humorists, French's writing seemed to
lose a lot of its character when he tried to write verses entirely
serious like these. On the other hand, in French's best songs,
such as "Paddy Reilly", "The Mountains of Mourne" and
"Little Brigid Flynn" there runs a vein of pathos which adds
greatly to the effect: but the sentiment he introduces is never
maudlin because, with the reserve of his class, it is balanced with
humour. It was this splendid quality which the publishers at
first failed to observe in "The Mountains of Mourne".

LITTLE BRIGID FLYNN

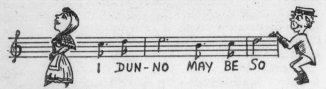

I DUN-NO   MAY BE SO

I've a nice slated house and a cow or two at grass,
I've a plant garden running by the door;
I've a shelter for the hens and a stable for the ass,
And what can a man want more.
I dunno, maybe so,
And a bachelor is aisy and he's free,
But I've lots to look after,
And I'm living all alone,
And there's no one looking after me.

Me father often tells me I should go and have a try
To get a girl that owns a bit of land;
I know the way he says it that there's someone in his eye,
And me mother has the whole thing planned.
I dunno, may be so,
And 'twould molify them greatly to agree,
But there's little Brigid Flynn,
Sure its her I want to win,
Though she never throws an eye at me.

Oh! there's a little girl who is worth her weight in gold,
An' that's a dacent dowry don't you see;
And I mean to go and ax her as soon as I get bold,
If she'll come and have an eye to me.
I dunno—will she go,
But I'd like to have her sittin' on me knee,
And I'd sing like a thrush,
On a hawthorn bush
If she'll come and have an eye to me.

After some appearances in Canada, the entertainers opened in the Mendelssohn Hall, New York on the 4th of November, to a splendid reception and thereafter gave their "Unique Recitals, Humours of Art and Music" in other American centres before completing the tour with engagements at Bermuda, the West Indies and Panama en route to England.

There are a couple of souvenirs in the way of songs resulting from the American tour—one of them "The Oklahoma Rose", which French originally incorporated in a humorous sketch; and "That's why we're Burying Him".

The second shows the American influence, for the lyric has a distinct music-hall echo, when compared with many of the vintage songs.

THE OKLAHOMA ROSE

1. All round de moon clouds are hangin' high an' hazy;
       On de lagoon moonbeams are lyin' lazy.
   Dat's when dis coon's g'wine to meet ma Maisie,
       An' I'm singin' de same old song.
   It's not about ma Dinah 'way down in Carolina,
       Ma latest love is finer, dan any flow'r dat blows.
   In fact, she don't remind me of gals I've left behind me,
       For true love's chains dey bind me to Oklahoma's Rose.

Chorus:

   She can trip like moonbeams on de water;
       Ev'ry step dis colour'd coon he taught her.
   Just one clip around her waist I caught her
       When de band play'd "Mumbling Mose".
   She's ma rose, ma lily an' ma daisy;
       Where she goes the coloured coons go crazy.
   All I know is ma Aminta Maisie
       Am de Oklahoma Rose.

2. All through de day she keeps lookin' down demurely,
        'Much as to say "I can't be a woman surely!
    I still can play with ma doll securely,
        For dis ain't de time to spoon."
    But when de sun am sinkin' her eyes begin a winkin'
        An' den I know she's thinkin' of dis yer colour'd coon.
    Oh! ain't I glad I found her. In love chains I have bound her.
        Her face is rather rounder—it's rounder dan de moon.

                            Chorus.

3. She hears me call an' she comes a-creepin', creepin',
        Over de wall she sees me leapin', leapin',
    Big folks an' small quietly are sleepin',
        When I meet ma lily belle.
    Up an' down de ladder I'm slippin' like a shadder,
        No one could be gladder dan me, I don't suppose.
    I'm coaxin' her an' teasin', I'm kissin' her an' squeezin',
        It seems to me it's pleasin' to Oklahoma's Rose.

        *   *   *   *   *

THAT'S WHY WE'RE BURYING HIM

Jim Maloney told a crony
Whom he met at "Isle de Coney"
That Wellington and Boney were a fool to him.
He'd like to have a tussle
With a man of Johnson's muscle,
So his friends arranged a meeting between Jack and Jim.

            Chorus:
            That's why we're burying him;
            That's why the poor man's dead.
            That's why we're hurrying him
            Off to his last long bed.
            One smite from Johnson's right
            Caught Maloney's head;
            That's why the poor man's dead.

Mick Maguire join'd a choir
But the height of his desire
Was to sing the tenor solo in a concert hall.
He practised "Pagliacci,"
As he heard the airs were catchy,
The piano played a prelude, and he gave one bawl!

> *Chorus:*
> That's why we're burying him;
> That's why the poor man's dead.
> That's why we're hurrying him
> Off to his last long bed.
> One yelp! then cries for help,
> As the eggs flew round his head;
> That's why the poor man's dead.

It was Carrie said to Harry,
"You will find that when we marry
I can cook the Sunday dinner when the maid's away".
"Oh, no dear," he entreated;
But his efforts were defeated,
And poor Harry had to eat it on the fatal day!

> *Chorus:*
> That's why we're burying him;
> That's why the poor man's dead.
> That's why we're hurrying him
> Off to his last long bed.
> One chew at the Irish stew,
> And the patient spirit fled;
> That's why the poor man's dead.

Frisco Foss he stole a "hoss",
And ere they strung him up, the boss
Said, "If any girl will marry him, the man goes free".
Then up came widow Twankey,
She was lean and she was lanky,
And says she, "Kind sir, I'll thanky, hand him down to me."

Chorus:

That's why we're burying him;
That's why the poor man's dead.
That's why we're hurrying him
Off to his last long bed.
One glance at his only chance,
Then, "String me up!" he said;
That's why the poor man's dead.

There are some interesting sidelights to "That's why we're
Burying Him". It was one occasion when the collaborators French
and Collisson failed to agree. Collisson wrote a tune with no
words and wanted sentimental words to fit it. French didn't care
for the requested type of lyric, but the tune suggested these
which Collisson wouldn't agree to. French proposed to his
daughter, Ettie, that she might write a new tune for the words,
which she did. So, in 1912, the name of one of his daughters
appeared for the first time as a composer—a sign that the family
were growing up.

One of the great difficulties of stage life, and often a cause of
tragedy, is that those involved in it cannot spend more time with
their families. If separated they may drift apart: if the children
travel with the parents they may never have the settling influence
of a proper home, or have anything beyond a scanty education.
The Frenches were lucky; they were a closely bound family.
Helen French, after the amateur occasion on which she met her
husband, never took an active part in stage life. She established
a home in London for the children and Willie, (as she always
knew him). With memories of his own happy childhood "among
the trackless woods at Clooneyquinn" it was a haven. Like all
people who are simple at heart, Willie French loved the company
of children, particularly his own, when he could steal time from
his show time travels to be with them. When he couldn't he
remembered them in a birthday verse.

Oh! Joan, when first you saw the light you caused us much annoy,
For both your parents thought you might as well have been a boy.

We HAD two daughters, each a gem—so thought—
Oh! was it strange?
We'd had about enough of them—
A boy would be a change.

But after standing you for ten long years of Peace and War.
If you were to be born again we'd want you—As you are.

DADDY

In after years Molly, the eldest of the children, in turn remembered her father and set several of his lyrics to music, which they
did not have in his time. One was the charming "Ach, I dunno"
which up to then had been a recitation for seemingly shy young
ladies, who were contemplating marriage—used by the lady
assistants who helped him from time to time.

"ACH, I DUNNO!"

I'm simply surrounded by lovers,
Since Da made his fortune in land;
They're comin' in crowds like the plovers
To ax for me hand.
There's clerks and policemen and teachers,
Some sandy, some black as a crow;
Ma says ye get used to the creatures,
But, ach, I dunno!

The convent is in a commotion
To think of me taking a spouse,
And they wonder I hadn't the notion
Of taking the vows.
'Tis a beautiful life and a quiet,
And keeps ye from going below,
As a girl I thought I might try it,
But, ach, I dunno!

I've none but meself to look after,
An' marriage it fills me with fears;
I think I'd have less of the laughter
And more of the tears.
I'll not be a slave like me mother,
With six of us all in a row,
Even one little baby's a bother,
But, ach, I dunno!

There's a lad that has taken me fancy,
I know he's a bit of a limb,
And though marriage is terrible chancy,
I'd—chance it with him,
He's coming to-night—oh—I tingle,
From the top of me head to me toe;
I'll tell him I'd rather live single,
But, ach, I dunno!

Constant travelling, and the strain of performance, had begun to tell on him a little, so, having decided that an assistant would be necessary in order to have an occasional "breather", he thought a lady might give more variety to the evening.

So, one at a time, Florence Marks, Betty Duncan, and, in later years, May Laffan helped him out on many engagements. Sometimes he would still do the performance solo—on visits to large boys' schools, for instance. One particular past pupil of Clongowes Wood College in County Kildare remembers the sketching and recitations and funny yarns with great nostalgia and affection; and, an interesting point, recalls snatches of a song which has not otherwise been recorded.

The name of this is "Luke the Looney" and this is all that can, so far, be traced, except that it appears in a programme of 1914 as a "new" song. It was probably written in that year.

LUKE THE LOONEY

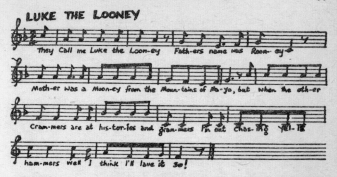

They call me Luke the Loon-ey Fath-ers name was Roon-ey
Moth-er was a Moon-ey from the Moun-tains of Ma-yo, but when the oth-er
Cram-mers are at his-tor-ies and gram-mers I'm out chas-ing yel-le
ham-mers well I think I'll lave it so!

French was, of course, notedly casual, and despite diligent searching through his papers by several hands, there are probably still a few numbers which he wrote and sang; which he carelessly filed, or did not file at all, and which have not come to light.

It is known, for instance, that there was music to these verses, probably written during or as a result of, the American visit, but it cannot now be recalled.

RAFTING DOWN THE RIO

Come sit beside the fire, old friend,
And dream that bamboo stems
Have risen up around us
'Mid flowers that shine like gems.
And we are back in fairyland,
And thro' the golden haze
We're rafting down the Rio—
In the old Jamaica days.

Oh! the old Jamaica days!
Faintly through that leafy maze
Comes the croon of Creole melodies
As down the stream one strays;
Till the fireflies sparkle round us
In those darkened water ways,
And we're rafting down the Rio—
In the old Jamaica days.

In those mighty mountain ranges
What memories lie hid,
Through the stricken street of Kingston
Stalks the ghost of Captain Kidd.
While a phantom Henry Morgan
Sets Port Royal in a blaze,
As we're rafting down the Rio—
In the old Jamaica days.

Oh! the old Jamaica days!
How we used to lie and laze,
And think of people working
As a curious kind of craze;
Wear and tear of brain and muscle
How we wondered if it pays,
As we rafted down the Rio—
In the old Jamaica days.

There's a terror in the tree tops,
And where the shadows brood,
For the wild cat and the scorpion
And the snakes are seeking food.
The alligators blink at us,
From fever-haunted bays,
And the woods knew Devil worship—
In the old Jamaica days.

Oh! the old Jamaica days!
When the sun's mid-winter rays
Have failed to pierce the fogs that fill
Our murky alley ways,
We'll sit beside the fire, old friend,
And as the embers blaze,
Go rafting down the Rio—
In the old Jamaica days.

The tune of a very early song only came into light again during
the completion of this book. I was searching for the words of

"Tullinahaw", and a friend of mine in Cork mentioned a gentleman whom he had heard singing it when on holidays in the west last year. I wrote off to the gentleman concerned, Mr. Vincent Shields of Loughrea, and although in the meantime "Tullinahaw" had turned up elsewhere found that Mr. Shields actually remembered "The Killyran Wrackers" as well.

He recorded the tune on a tape and sent it to me. So, here it is in print for the first time.

THE KILLYRAN WRACKERS

But from the field of glory there came another story and Colonel Kit Magorey gave me to understand at Alma, Balaclava and at Course at Inkerman There was nothing like the wrackers from the Town of Killyran.

Now this is the story
Of the boys who left our village,
Under Kit Magorey—that military man.
Some they go for glory,
And some they go for pillage,
And the latter was the motive with the boys of Killyran.

But from the field of glory
There came another story,
And Colonel Kit Magorey
Gave me to understan'
At Alma, Balaclava, and, of course, at Inkerman
There was nothing like the Wrackers
From the town of Killyran.
The mob that took the Malakoff, and also the Redan,
Was the crowd from Casey's corner in the town of Killyran.

They tell me that Boney,
At Waterloo was winning,
And so he would have, only the Prussians lent a hand,
Says Boney, "Alone I
Would send the Britons spinning,
But I cannot stand the music of that Blucher's German Band!"

But from the field of glory
There came another story
And Colonel Kit Magorey
Gave me to understan'
Says Boneyparte "My veterans have done what mortals can
But they couldn't face the Wrackers from the town of Killyran!
It's not that Sepoy General who spoilt my finest plan,
It's that regiment of reffiians from the town of Killyran!"

They tell me that Great Britain
Is soon to be undone,
In the "Daily Mail" 'tis written
And so it must be true.
A great big German army comes annihilating London,
While "Bobs"* and all his regulars are beaten black and blue.

But from the field of glory
Will come another story
And Colonel Kit Magorey
Gives me to understan'
No foe will ever face us, if only in the van
Is that mob of malefactors from the town of Killyran.
And if the Kaiser ever tries the flame of war to fan,
Berlin will be bombarded by the Boys of Killyran.

This song was written shortly before the 1914/18 war, and is
much in the tradition of the songs of "martial glory" which he
was writing in the early 90's—'tho' his heroes might be scapegraces
mostly "on the make", they could turn up trumps when the occasion
demanded, or at least so they said when they came home!

May Laffan is also known to have sung "Innismeela" but the
music was lost. Philip Green restored it to the French repertoire
by writing a new tune in 1962.

*Roberts, the English military hero of the Boer War.

INNISMEELA

I can only see the moonbeams that on Innismeela float,
But if I slept inside the fairies ring
I could see them sailing, sailing in their little boat,
And I'd hear the song the little people sing.
For the Fairy Man has told me how he slumbered there one day,
And woke to find them dancing on the shore,
And still he hears them singing, though 'tis faint and far away,
And he's wishing he was with them evermore.

I've seen the Queen of Fairyland! I've heard her wondrous song,
With her to heights of happiness I've flown;
Now I know the days are dreary, now I know the nights are long,
For the one I love has left me all alone.
Innismeela! Innismeela! there's a sleep that knows no dream,
And it's in that dreamless slumber I shall be,
For I know that I shall waken by some still celestial stream
And through the golden light she'll come to me.

Times had changed; the long Victorian reign had ended, and
the short and gay Edwardian era had followed it into history in
the summer of 1910. The changing times were reflected in some
of the songs.

The young engineer of Cavan days had travelled around in a
pony and trap, and, a friend of the pioneer Macredy, had been
wildly up-to-date with the latest things in bicycles. There is no
doubt that, despite the greater convenience of quicker modes of
travel, French liked the quiet leisurely atmosphere now passing,
and his successive songs about noisy new inventions, "Jim
Wheelahan's Automobeel" (1903), "Maguire's Motor Bike"
(1906), and "Flanagan's Flying Machine" (1911) almost invariably predicted disaster.

The "Automobeel" was so new in these days as to be a
curiosity, while Bleriot's flight across the channel from Calais
to Dover in 1909 seemed to epitomise all that was marvellous
of the coming age.

JIM WHEELAHAN'S AUTOMOBEEL

JIM WHEELAHANS AUTOMOBEEL

When Jim Wheelahan made
All his money in trade,
He said he'd astonish the town;
And he stuck to his word
As you'll say when you've heard
Of the wonderful yoke he brought down.
'Twas the latest design
In the motor-car line,
Parisian and very genteel—
A motor might do
For me or for you,
But this was an Automobeel!

> *Chorus:*
> Jim Wheelahan's Automobeel!
> Oh! that was the Tatherin' wheel.
> He telegraphed down
> He would ride through the town
> Next day in his Automobeel!

He steered her until
He came nigh the long hill,
And he smiled as he rolled her along;
But the smile it gave way
To a look of dismay
When he found that the brake had gone wrong.
His father came out
To give him a shout:
Jim met him half-ways down the hill
And the last thing he said
As they put him to bed
Was "Hould on till I alther me will."

Chorus:
Oh! Wheelahan's Automobeel!
It knocked the man head over heel;
It was only wan touch,
But he walks with a crutch
Since he met with the Automobeel!

We'd the band on a stand
And the town all on hand,
But they fled when he entered the square—
The beautiful stand
And the Emmett Brass Band
Was knocked to the divil knows where!
Blind "Danny the Duck"
Had the worst bit of luck,
For the dog in the string it got furled;
And they found him full stritch
On his back in the ditch,
Lamentin' the end of the world!

Chorus:
When they said 'twas the Automobeel,
As they carried him home in a creel,
Says he, with a curse,
"I wish 'twas his hearse
Instead of his Automobeel!"

Now I'd have you to note
That the quarryman's goat
Had been unwell that same night,
So for breakfast that day
She had just put away
A canful of strong dynamite.
Having taken her load,
She lay down on the road—
Even goats must digest such a meal!—
And she didn't observe
Comin' sharp round the curve
Jim Wheelahan's Automobeel!

Chorus:

> A bump! an explosion! a squeal!—
> We buried his hat and one wheel.
> He's at rest—so are we,
> For the country is free
> From Wheelahan's Automobeel!

ENCORE VERSE:

Jim Wheelahan's ghost
Took a run round the coast
On the day of the motor-car race,
And the wind bein' fair,
He was "whooshed" thro' the air
At a rate even Edge daren't face.
When the winner came up
To receive the great cup,
His anger he could not conceal,
For there at the post
Was Jim Wheelahan's ghost,
Wid three-fourths of his Automobeel!

Chorus:

> Says Edge, "Be the laws, I'll appeal!
> Such a record could never be real!"
> Here the cock gave a crow,
> And Jim vanished below,
> With the ghost of his Automobeel!

FLANAGAN'S FLYING MACHINE

'Twas Flanagan found out the secret of flight,
And made such a perfect affair,
That Farman and Bleriot, Latham and White
Proclaimed him the King o' the air.

And, mind, you, I think he deserved his success
For really he worked very hard;
Six days out of seven his private address
Was—the Hospital Accident Ward.
But soon he was safe and serene
And every day could be seen
By admiring crowds,
Leppin' over the clouds
In his marvellous flying machine.

Said the Kaiser—"On Britain I'm going to pounce
Like a terrier dog on a rat".
Said his officers—"Do, and you'll get the grand bounce,
For you're talking too much through your hat."
Said the Kaiser—"There's nothing on earth you'll allow
My army and fleet can defy."
Said his officers—"Nothin' on earth, sire, but how
About something up there in the sky?"
Said the Kaiser—"I know what you mean
Though faith! I'd forgotten it clean,
The war is postponed
While the atmosphere's owned
By Flanagan's flying machine"

Mrs. Bryan was bringing her baby along
To be christened Patricia Kathleen,
When over the hill, on its way to Hong Kong
Came Flanagan's flying machine.
Says poor Mrs. Bryan "Oh! was that a bat?
Or a big dragon fly that I seen",
Says Bryan "Och, woman, go long out o' that
It was Flanagan's flyin' machine".
Oh, Flanagan's flyin' machine!
When she handed his riv'rence the wean
'Twas no wonder he smiled,
When he said "Name this child"
She said "Flanagan's flyin' machine"

The King and the Queen were enjoyin' a drive,
When their motor broke down by the way;
And the Queen said "Oh Murther!
We'll never arrive
In time for me afthernoon tay"
Then Tim came along in his aeroplane
And, whoosin' them up in the air,
Had the two of them back in Balmoral again
Wid a cuple of minutes to spare.
And the King he remarked to the Queen,
"Was iver the like of it seen?"
"Tim! ye Divil," he said,
"Take the crown oft my head,
But give me yer flying machine."

In 1913 he got an engagement which provided an abiding memory—a working holiday in the hotels of Switzerland amongst the snows and the skis, and in sight of the Jungfrau. This is the mountain which, viewed from a certain angle, and in the right light, has the appearance of a girl's face in repose. It intrigued him; he painted it often, and afterwards used it as one of the tricks in his stage act—an addition to his "upside down" sketches.

One of the greatest pleasures I have had in relation to Percy French (and he has given me many) was the good fortune of being able to unearth the only one of his lightning chalk sketches known to still exist in a second hand shop, and present it, if in a battered condition, to his daughters, who had been hoping to find one for years. It was the Jungfrau. Goodness knows how many of these sketches were given away, or thrown away, by the entertainer in his time. A few may lie forgotten in somebody's lumber room, but being sketches of such a temporary nature—chalk on paper—it is unlikely that they have survived unless a special effort was made to preserve them. The only ones previously in possession of his family, proudly hanging on a wall, were "dusted" by a maid one morning and that was that! Percy French always hoped to return to Switzerland, but a proposed holiday the following year with his family was postponed when war broke out.

The war also disrupted Percy French's life as an entertainer. Quite early on he went to France with Collisson to entertain the troops. His own particular brand of satiric comment was a little less gentle than usual when dealing with a Kaiser whose main underlying error in French's eye, apart from the atrocities of which his armies were then being accused, was in being faulted as a sportsman and a gentleman.

"AM TAG"

(TO THE DAY)

For years I have heard a curious word,
    'Tis German, I'm told, for the Day;
"Am Tag" it is spelt, and to Saxon or Kelt
    A thread it is meant to convey.
It means the dread hour when Germany's power
    Shall pull down Britannia's Flag,
And Kings will Kow-tow to old Billy Bow-bow,
    That's what Germany means by "Am Tag".

Refrain:

Oh Bill, with the bluster and brag,
    You may rage at that "little red rag";
I'll bet you a crown that you don't pull it down,
    For all your tall talk and "Am Tag"

"You are arming for war," cried Bill to the Czar,
    "An' what if I am" said old Nick;
"Oh, nothing," said Bill, "If you will, sure you will,
    But I call it a scoundrelly trick."
"I could flatten out France, and then there's a chance
    Of adding John Bull to my bag;
But the Belgians and you 'leppen' out at me too,
    Is playing the puck with 'Der Tag'."

Refrain:
"But," says he, with his bounce and his brag,
     As he flourished his freak of a flag,
"I'll sit cheek by jowl on Windsor, yer sowl,
     With this double-faced fowl on 'Der Tag!' "

So he trained every one to handle a gun,
     And kept them three years at their drill;
But they never could hit a haystack if it
     Didn't keep most uncommonly still.
"Keep charging *en masse*," said the Kaiser; "alas,
     If they shoot you, die for the flag;
There are millions behind, so I really don't mind
     How many they shoot on 'Der Tag'."

Refrain:
Oh Bill, with your bounce and your brag,
     There are ghosts at your carriage wheels drag,
And the victims that call from Louvain's blackened wall
     Will hasten your fall on "Der Tag!"

You may train up your sons to be latter-day Huns,
     But we'll catch you and cage you at last;
For you've proved such a pest that no nation can rest
     Till Prussia's a thing of the past.
The God that you prized was the devil disguised,
     And while you sail under his flag
There is rapine and loot for each beer-sodden brute,
     But we'll send in the bill on "Der Tag."

Refrain:
But it's no time to boast or to brag,
     While the pendulum's still on the wag;
The peril's not passed, to the Standard fly fast,
     Or we'll ne'er hear the last of "Am Tag!"

French apparently thought that "Tag" rhymed with "drag",
"brag" etc., which, of course, it doesn't.

ALL BY THE BALTIC SAY

ONCE THERE WAS A KY- SER WHOSE HEAD WAS OF GREAT SIZE, SIR

Once there was a Kyser
    Whose head was of great size, sir,
And lived by telling lies, sir,
    All by the Baltic Say.

He'd wire to Pretoria
    "Dear Kruger I implore ye
Knock spots off Queen Victoria
    All by the Baltic Say."

And when the Queen resinted
    Such conduct, he repinted
An' said he never mint it
    All by the Baltic Say.

He'd an army of five millions
    Who treated all civilians
As low and vulgar villyans
    All by the Baltic Say.

Sez he "Me proper station
    And natural vocation
Is King of all creation
    All by the Baltic Say."

"I'll mobilize me Prooshans
    And send them dirty Rooshans
To finish their ablutions
    All by the Baltic Say,"

"All treaties I'm evadin'
    An' with high Heaven aidin'
In blood I'll soon be wadin'
    All by the Baltic Say."

But Belgium said "I bar you"
    And Britain said "I dar you"
And France said, "Vell vare are you?"
    All by the Baltic Say.

So while his army waited
    Till Liege was occupated
His plans they were frustrated
    All by the Baltic Say.

The great siege guns they thunder'd
    The Germans kill'd and plunder'd,
But soon they found they'd blunder'd
    All by the Baltic Say.

For men who go to battle
    Like droves of driven cattle
Feel bad when bullets rattle
    All by the Baltic Say.

An' now that they've retreated,
    Dishearten'd and defeated,
They'll not be so conceited
    All by the Baltic Say.

The officers called "Yunkers"
    May not be quite such funkers
But they are well named "Young Curs"
    All by the Baltic Say.

And hymns of peace will rise, sir
    From Europe to the sky, sir
When there shall be no Kyser
    All by the Baltic Say.

Of these two songs, now period pieces, "All by the Baltic Say" was the more popular. Maybe "Am Tag" was a little too near the grim situation in line of thought for a comic song. It has always been notable that the most successful war songs have little to do with the war situation itself. "All by the Baltic Say" was sung as a duet with Florence Marks in the style of an old time "Come-all-ye"—the popular name for the ballad of innumerable verses which can be often heard in a public house and almost always starts with a line such as—"Come-all-ye gallant gentlemen and listen to my song".

French was fond of writing parodies and one of his cleverest is another take-off of a "Come-all-ye", to be sung unaccompanied. In this type of song, usually compiled by an amateur ballad maker, the singer sometimes has difficulty in fitting all the words into one line, and this is cleverly suggested by French.

COME-ALL-YE

Oh! a sailor courted a farmer's daughter;
Who lived contagious to the Isle of Man,
With warbling melodies he did besought her
To marry him before she'd marry any other sort of a kind of a man.

But the farmer's daughter had great possessions,
A silver teapot and two pounds in gold;
And says she, "Would ye marry me, me bould salt water sea-sailor,
If I threw them into the ocean cold?"

"Oh", says he, "I'd marry you, me heart's enchantment,
If you had nothing but your father's curse!"
So she made up a bundle of all her grand possessions
And threw them into the water . . . that ends that verse.

But the sailor he could swim like a duckling,
So into the water he dived down deep below,
Got hold of the bundle and swam away chuckling,
To think of the times he'd be having when he landed down in
Ballinasloe.

But the farmer's daughter was kilt with the laughing,
To think of the bundle she'd made up out of a stone . . .
Oh! a sailor courted a farmer's daughter,
But now he's wishing that he'd left the girl alone.

French also sometimes parodied well-known ballads as when
he wrote "The Mary Ann McHugh" as a take-off of "The Cruise
of the Calabar"—which itself had been written to the tune of a
genuine old ballad called "Limerick is Beautiful".

Other parodies were "Flaherty's Drake" (a much varied version
of the older Ned, or Nell, Flaherty's Drake) and the "Next
Landing of the French". The latter was based on an old Irish
ballad from United Irishmen times, of which there were many
conflicting versions, called the Shan Van Vocht (i.e. Sean Bhean
Bhocht, or Poor Old Woman, meaning Ireland.) The usual
version starts "The French are on the Say, says the Shan Van
Vocht" and Percy used this theme to mean himself, as "French",
and the rest of the parody to explain his act. This was written
more to advertise the act in advance publicity than as an actual
performing piece.

THE MARY ANN McHUGH

Come all ye lads who plough the seas and also seize the plough,
The cruise of a canal boat I am telling to ye now.
It was the Mary Ann McHugh that braved the angry surf
And bore away from Mullingar with a terrible load of turf.

And the captain's name was Duff,
His manners they were rough,
But every cape and headland by its Christian name he knew,
And he issued this command—
"Keep her well in sight of land!
Till we make the port of Dublin in the Mary Ann McHugh."

The engine was of one horse-power; propelled wid a black-thorn
stick,
Wid the wind astarn, and filled with corn, the horse went a
terrible lick.
We worked her round the Hill o' Down, and then Kilcock we
passed,
And when we seen John Flynn's Shebeen, we cried out "Land
at Last".

But the captain, Jamsey Duff,
Cried "Luff! ye lubbers, luff!
And don't put in near Johnny Flynn
Whatever else ye do.
Last time we passed his door
We forgot to pay his score,
So he's got the polis watching for the Mary Ann McHugh."

Then up and spake an old sailor who had sailed the Irish sea.
"I pray thee put into yonder port or the crew will mutinee:
To put to sea with the boy and me is a cruel thing, I think,
With water, water everywhere, and never a drop o' drink!"

But the captain, Jamsey Duff,
Said "Enough, my lad, enough!
No man before the mast shall ever tell me what to do.
Clap on all sail at wance,
For that's our only chance,
To keep from debt and danger in the Mary Ann McHugh."

With anxious hearts the vessel starts upon her altered course,
The wind and waves they lashed the shore, and the pilot lashed
the horse,
But all in vain—beneath the strain the rope began to part,
And she ran aground on a lump of coal that wasn't put down in
the chart.

And the captain, Jamsey Duff,
He caught me such a cuff,
And then he said, "Go heave the lead," while the flag at
                                        half-mast flew,
But I had enough
Of the tyrant, Jamsey Duff,
So I heaved the lead at his head and fled from the Mary Ann
                                             McHugh.

FLAHERTY'S DRAKE

Oh, I'm come here before ye
To tell yez a story;
At the narrative gory
Your heart it will quake:
For this is the history,
Chock full of mystery,
Of the black murder of Flaherty's drake.

Now when Flaherty died
He called me to his side:
Says he:—"This divide
Of the farm I'll make:
The house goes to Biddy,
She's honest and steady
And you'll take the stock, that's four ducks and a drake."

Chorus:

Quack, quack, quack, went the ducks upon his track,
As they followed him down to the shore;
They may quack, quack, quack, he's never comin' back
No, he's never comin' back no more.

That night when in bed
In the loft overhead
The door of the shed
Gave a sort of a crake—
"Get up man!" says Biddy—
That's Flaherty's widdy—
"I think 'tis the voice of Ned Flaherty's drake."
Now with that remark
I leapt up in the dark,
And ran like a lark
To the shore of the lake;
And there 'twas I found it,
Its four wives around it;
Some blackguard had drowned
Ned Flaherty's drake.

Chorus:

Quack, quack, quack, etc.

I made such a din
That the neighbours came in:
Says Councillor Flynn:
"Depositors I'll take
Build up a large fire
And then we'll enquire
What caused the demayse of Ned Flaherty's drake."
When the coroner sat
On the bird, says he: "Pat,
'Tis tender and fat
What a meal it would make."
And then, never mindin'
The tears my eyes blindin',
They roasted and dined on
Ned Flaherty's drake.

Chorus:

Quack, quack, quack, etc.

THE NEXT LANDING OF THE FRENCH

1.   Oh! the French is on the say,
                Says the Shan Van Vocht,
He'll be here widout delay,
                Says the Shan Van Vocht.
He's been gone for many a day,
By them Saxons led asthray,
Och, sure them's the boys can pay!
                Says the Shan Van Vocht.

2.   He has all his latest jokes,
                Says the Shan Van Vocht.
And he draws wid lightning strokes,
                Says the Shan Van Vocht.
And that song wid quaint refrain,
Of "The Clare Excursion Train."
You will want to hear again
                Says the Shan Van Vocht.

3.   How could Irish songs be sung?
                Says the Shan Van Vocht.
Will he try the ancient tongue?
                Says the Shan Van Vocht.
Oh! the Irish may be grand
But the tongue at his command,
Is the one we understand,
                Says the Shan Van Vocht.
Tho' the Green Isle of the West
May have brought him many a jest,
'Tis the land he loves the best:
                Says the Shan Van Vocht.

In England, French, with Collisson, performed in aid of war charities, without religious discrimination. One of their best remembered was in aid of a London Catholic Charity Bazaar, where it was intended that they would do two numbers on the way to a remunerative engagement. A heavy air raid intervened; the other artists couldn't turn up and French and the little doctor couldn't leave. So, they stayed on, and gave a full two hours show, continuing even while the raid was at its worst. This kindness was remembered by the Catholic community of the district in after years when the two entertainers died, and numerous Masses were offered for them at the parish Church in Quex Street, N.W.

Percy's nature could absorb such experiences when they came along, and help to soothe others as well—

"Wasn't that the pleasantest raid we ever had?" was his calm comment when it was over.

Maybe this was the concert for which he wrote "Larry Mick McGarry", the last song he is known to have composed.

He had been going over it for days and changing it here and there, and when the great night came the family were naturally anxious to know how it had gone. He had remembered to give the cook a ticket, and as she stamped downstairs on her return the only comment was, "He did that oul' song he's been practisin' up there for the last days on end!" Prophets are seldom appreciated in their own country, and neither are entertainers. Unlike the rest of the audience she'd heard it before.

LARRY MICK McGARRY

Oh! Larry Mick McGarry
Was the torment of the town,
A lad a woman's glad o'
But a man would like to drown;
With a smile he would beguile away
A girl from her boy,
An' before he got a mile away
He tired of his toy.

Chorus:
Titheryah the doodle ah
No marryin' for me!
Titheryah the doodle ah
As far as I can see.
Bright by the candle light
An' pourin' out the tea,
But yer glad ye didn't ax her
In the mornin'

Oh, Larry played old Harry
With the girls about the place,
At the dancin' they'd be glancin'
At the features of his face,
But he never would endeavour
To be lover-like until
Mary Carey, she's a fairy,
Had him goin' like a mill.

Chorus:

Titheryah the doodle ah
He met her in the street,
Titheryah the doodle ah
Sez he, "Yer lookin' sweet.
A walk an' a talk wid you
I think would be a treat,
But all he got from Mary was,
"Good morning!"

The dancin' down at Clancy's
Brought in all the neighbourhood,
Though the roof wasn't waterproof,
The floor was fairly good;
An' Larry Mick McGarry
He could handle well the leg,
But Mary, light an' airy,
Oh, she took him down a peg.

Chorus:

Titheryah the doodle ah
She footed it wid Flynn
Titheryah the doodle ah
An' all the other min.
But Larry Mick McGarry
Oh! he hadn't a look in,
Faith he had to go and find her
In the morning.

Oh, she taught him till she brought him
Up to where she had designed
Sez Larry, "Will ye marry me?"
Sez she, "I wouldn't mind"
He kissed her an' carrissed her
Which is quite the proper thing
Then together, hell for leather
They were off to buy a ring.

Chorus:
Titheryah the doodle ah
"No marryin' ", sez you,
Titheryah the doodle ah
Ye may escape the 'flu
Wait till you meet yer mate
An' all there is to do
Is to go an' buy the licence
In the morning.

The war changed many things, and certainly made it more
difficult for those engaged in theatrical business to continue as
they had done. French was no exception—indeed his kind of
entertainment, being often of a semi-private nature, was more
affected than most; so, not unpleasantly, he found himself spending
more time within reach of the beloved bogs and streams of his
native country, where everyday life had not been so affected by
the war.

In the summertime he principally played at seaside places in
series of one-night stands (two nights in some of the larger places
like Portrush), but also performed in the larger centres, and, in
Dublin tried a revival of the "Dublin-up-to-Date" idea when,
in 1916 he brought out a revue called "How Dublin does it".

The name of Percy French was now such a familiar one that
he was called on for all sorts of functions. In Kilkee, for instance,
as judge of a fishing contest where, local tradition relates, he
caused consternation (he could never take such things seriously)
by stuffing a weight down the throat of a fish small enough to

be thrown back and declaring it the winner. He was a good sportsman himself, with a natural aptitude for games, but could never understand people being all that anxious about winning.

NO MORE O' YER GOLFIN' FOR ME

Through life I have played all the games that one can,
At football I played on the good Gaelic plan,
You *may* miss the ball but you *must* kick the man,
Or else it won't count to your score.
At Cricket they never knew what I'd be at,
My very first welt laid the bowler out flat,
As they hadn't another I carried me bat,
While they carried him home on a door.

> *Chorus:*
>
> Golf! Golf! Carry me off!
> Bury me down by the sea.
> The putters may put, still I won't stir a fut,
> No more of yer golfin' for me.

I'm an old fashioned dog to be larnin' new tricks,
But Murphy came round wid two bags full o' sticks,
At Hockey you've one club, but here you have six,
And that's a remarkable thing.
Then Murphy drove off the wee ball. Oh! Begor!
It rose through the air, till it looked like a star,
The head of my driver'd have gone just as far,
If it hadn't been tied with a string.

> *Chorus:*
>
> Golf! Golf! Carry me off!
> Bury me down by the sea.
> The drivers may drive, but dead or alive,
> No more o' yer golfin' for me.

When I got to the bunker, of clubs I'd just two,
But one was a brass wan, sez I, "That'll do,
If the ball won't go over, I'll make it go through,"
So I slash'd and I hammer'd away.
Then Murphy came up, and sez he, "Ain't it grand,"
Says I, "It's a game I don't quite understand,
How much do they give here for shovellin' sand?
I'd like to get on by the day."

> *Chorus:*
>
> Golf! Golf! Carry me off!
> Bury me down by the sea.
> The lofters may loft,
> Still my sleep shall be soft,
> No more o' yer golfin' for me.

While I stood on the green, I heard some one cry "four"
I paid no attention—that wasn't my score,
I had done the nine holes in two hundred or more,
When a ball hit the back of my head.
With Maguire it's always a blow for a blow,
I had just one club left—as I wheeled on my foe,
'Twas a beautiful lady. Begor! 'twas no go.
"Did you see where the ball fell?" she said.

Spoken:—

"Did I see?"

"No! I hadn't seen it exactly, but I understood it was somewhere adjacent. In fact to the best of my incapacity it was somewhere contagious."

I was goin' to pick it up and give it to her, when she said: "Oh! don't touch it. That's a lovely lie!"

Of course, when she said that, I saw she knew all about my broken head, so I told her how I'd laid off to give her a welt across the face.

That made us quite friendly at once, so I took her out of the firing line for a bit and axed her if we could not make a match of it.

She said her match was Colonel Bogey!

"Oh! thim soldiers! We ceevilians don't have a chance! ! !

> *Chorus:*
> Golf! Golf! Carry me off!
> Bury me down by the sea.
> All the wurrld may go
> To "Old Bogey!" but oh!
> No more of yer golfin' for me.

But now athletic days were over. The days of prolific writing were over too, because during the later years he wrote little, relying on the very large repertoire he had built up over forty years. The last published song, appropriately enough a lullaby to the children who occupied such a big part of his heart, came out in 1915, but had been written for "Noah's Ark" in 1907. The music was by J. A. Robertson.

PRETENDY LAND

> Oh! come little baby across the sea,
> Come to Pretendy land with me,
> There's jam for dinner and jam for tea,
> And sweeties come falling in show'rs.
> Where you need not think before you speak,
> But gabble and chatter and yell and shriek;
> Where lessons are only a minute a week,
> And play-time is hours and hours.
>
> Over the Blanket billow, over the sheets of sand,
> When night comes down on Counter-pane Town
> We sail to Pretendy land.
> Over the hills of Pillow
> By favouring breezes fanned,
> With the flag made fast to the bedpost mast
> We sail to Pretendy land.

Where fairies live in a lovely wood,
Not bad fairies, nor yet too good,
We'll play with Little Red Riding Hood,
And, also, with Little Boy Blue,
Where nobody's nasty and nobody's old,
And nobody's ever as good as gold,
And 'though you never do what you are told,
Yet nobody's cross with you.

Over the Blanket billow, over the Bolster strand,
Both eyes must close e're my baby goes
Away to Pretendy Land.
Over the Hills of Pillow,
Wandering hand in hand.
Not a sigh! not a sound!
Ah! baby has found
Her way to Pretendy Land.

The war years passed, and when the entertainment world
opened its doors fully again it found itself having to cater for an
overflow of audiences demanding amusement of as noisy and
shallow a nature as possible, so that four years of horror could
be forgotten.

It wasn't the world for a Percy French: all his instincts called
for a gentler one which had passed, but there was a core of steel
in this little man which showed itself, without fuss, at times of
need in his life.

He resumed his place in entertainment;
played a short season of Music-Hall which he
didn't care for very much. It catered for a
different type of audience, far removed from
the intimate atmosphere he liked to create: so
he went back, in some relief, to his own special
type of solo work. But, the constant strain was
beginning to tell. Early in 1920, when travelling
home from an engagement in Glasgow, he
was taken ill and, breaking the journey, made
his way to the home of his cousin and friend,
Canon Richardson, at Formby, Lancashire.

After an illness of about a week he died there, of heart failure, on January 24th, and was buried in the little Protestant churchyard at Formby.

Collisson died unexpectedly a week after conducting a burial service for his old colleague in London, so that even death did not long separate a partnership which had brought simple pleasure to the world for over a quarter of a century.

Percy French was 65, and had remained an undaunted trouper to the end.

*   *   *   *   *

It was almost inevitable that the works of Percy French would in some way suffer a decline after his death. Much of what was personal in his performance couldn't be conveyed by words or music: as E. V. Lucas has said "so much of the real man was incommunicable through what he left behind—it was so much a matter of voice, and expression and timing." This is always the way with a great artist, but, fortunately, Percy French's songs had a quality which, in the end, has enabled the best of them to survive. It was inevitable that some of the songs, or individual verses, would become outdated and fade, unlike "The Mountains of Mourne" which had become so established as to be accepted as part of the nation's balladry, and other numbers such as "Eileen Oge", "Brigid Flynn", "Phil the Fluther's Ball" which kept appearing with obstinate regularity at concerts, and on records and wireless programmes: but many of the other really good songs were slipping from regular memory.

His family never lost faith with his work.

Not long after he died his sister, Mrs. de Burgh Daly, edited a collection of his prose and poems which contained the words of many of the songs, and his daughter, Molly, as already mentioned, provided music for several lyrics, until her death some years ago, amongst them "Ballymilligan" (1952), to the traditional tune of "The Fisherman's Lament", and "On the Road to Ballybay" (1938).

BALLYMILLIGAN

Back to Ballymilligan, it's there that I would be,
Back to Ballymilligan beside the silver sea,
The wee white houses peeping out to greet the dawn o' day,
The little trawlers creeping out to fish below the bay.
Oh! If I had me will again it's there that I would be—
Back in Ballymilligan beside the silver sea.

They've paid me passage over—I've a gran'child on me knee
An' I'm living here in clover in the home they've made for me.
But it hasn't got the charm an' it hasn't got the view
Of the little hillside farm that my Danny brought me to.
Oh! to feel the thrill again when he was courting me
Back in Ballymilligan beside the silver sea.

I've been in Wanamakers, and in all the mighty stores,
That covers many acres and have forty diff'rent floors,
But it's down to Katy Ryan I'd be trav'lin' in me shoes,
To do me bit o' buyin' and to hear the neighbour's news,
To pay the weeshy bill agin, for sugar and for tea—
Back in Ballymilligan beside the silver sea.

No doubt I'd find a change in it, for time goes rollin' on,
I fancy I'd feel strange in it, the old companions gone;
But there is one that's sleeping there—the one that I love best;
Some day I may be creeping there to lay me down to rest.
An' then the old gray hill again will shelter him and me—
Back in Ballymilligan beside the silver sea.

ON THE ROAD TO BALLYBAY

"Is this the road to Ballybay?"
Sez I to Miss Magee;
"You're leavin' it behind you,"
Sez Maryanne to me.
So I turned and walked beside her,
And 'tis only fair to say
It was very pleasant walkin'
On the road to Ballybay.

> Ballybay, Ballybay,
> 'Twas a dark and winthry day,
> But the sun was surely shinin'
> On the road to Ballybay.

"Is this the road to fame and wealth?"
Sez I to Miss Magee;
"Ye've got the brains, ye've got the health,"
Sez Maryanne to me.
"But still I want a comrade
To praise me an' to blame,
An' keep me from the traps that's laid
Upon the road to fame."

> Ballybay, Ballybay,
> No man could go asthray
> With a guide like her beside him
> On the road to Ballybay.

"Is this the road to Paradise?"
Sez I to Miss Magee;
"I'm thinkin' that it might be,"
Sez Maryanne to me.
Oh, I saw the love-light leppin'
In a pair of roguish eyes,
An' I knew we two were steppin'
On the road to Paradise.

Ballybay, Ballybay,
The birds are far away;
But our hearts they sang together,
On the road to Ballybay.

Helen French maintained an interest in her husband's work
right up to the time when she too died at the age of 88, in 1956.
His remaining daughters, Ettie and Joan, have diligently collected
all possible information on their father's writings.

Strangely enough the development of new techniques in
recording brought the first signs of a real resurgence of interest
in the songs. A young Irish singer from Louth, Brendan
O'Dowda, made a long-play Percy French record which became
a best-seller.

Recordings by other artists followed, and some of the songs
found their way to a film soundtrack. Then, at Christmas of
1956, Radio Éireann broadcast a radio biography of the early
part of his life called "The Last Troubadour" by Donal Giltenan
with the Cork artist Chris Curran as Percy French. This awakened
such tremendous interest in the man himself in his own country,
that it was repeated several times, and Mr. Giltenan was en-
couraged to develop it into a musical play, with additional music
by Eric Rogers. "The Golden Years" ran at the Gaiety Theatre
Dublin for the whole summer of 1961, after playing some weeks
at Liverpool, and subsequently was presented at Cork, Belfast
and Galway. It had special performances in the little Connaught
town of Roscommon—where the people take great pride in the
work of their fellow-townsman, although the family link with
the district has now been broken for some time.

For many years before the turn of the century Willie's "little
nest" as he called it, among the rafters of his old home was kept
there for him, although he lived in Dublin, but the house is now
derelict. His father died in 1897 and the property passed to Willie's
eldest brother. He, and his son after him, made efforts to keep
the property, (the French girls remember bouncing along on
excursions to Clooneyquinn in their cousin's rather battered old
jalopy), but it was becoming uneconomic, so, some years ago,
they disposed of it.

Clooneyquinn represented a way of life which has passed, or, with large properties no longer easy to maintain, is passing,—a gracious life of afternoon tea and tennis parties on a summer's afternoon at the "Big House", to which the guests arrived in ponies and traps, or riding in carriages, rather than in the latest sports car. This was the background which produced Percy French and it influenced the changing pattern of his life. From the quiet seclusion of an Irish country home and enclosed circle of society, he found himself drifting into the hurly-

burly of show business, with the mixed bag of the world for an audience—playing a banjo and singing songs for a living; developing amateur enthusiasm to a professional competence which never lost its spontaneous air. Yet, through it all he never ceased to be a member of his own class, though his friends might range from the Lord Chancellor of Ireland to Planxty Kelly of Mayo, and his work revealed all the better qualities of that background—an acute but kind observation, well-balanced sense of humour, the nice ability of knowing what was right to say, and what was not: to which he added his own humanity, splendid turn of comic phrase, and affection for those people of the countryside about whom his best songs are written.

It is nice to feel that the songs, more popular than ever before, are accepted in his own country on their own valuation, for, Percy French, taken as a whole, represented these people who were his friends sympathetically and well. There are extravagances here and there, of course, as is inevitable in the absurdities of a comic song, but the characters in his songs come up quite clearly as the loveable people he intended them to be.

Val Vousden, himself a Gaelic enthusiast, had these thoughts in mind when, hearing the assembled thousands at a Hurling final at Croke Park (headquarters of the Gaelic Athletic Association) lifting their voices in "Come Home, Paddy Reilly", a lump came in his throat, and he wished that Percy French was there to hear.

The little man had been gone many years then, but he would like to know that his songs had been remembered. Maybe he never built any bridges, or did any of the things his father might have expected him to do; but he wrote his songs, and left them for us to sing, and our world is a better place for the gaiety and sympathy of William Percy French.

APPENDIX I.

SONGS NOT USED IN TEXT

(a) CORNELIUS BURKE

When first I took up arms, 'twas a faction-fight in Clare;
  The Burkes they all were there and faith they did their share!
My father said, "Cornelius, you've a mighty martial air—
  I think that you were cut out for a soldier!"

Chorus.

Then hurrah for the trumpet's sound!—
  But it don't fetch me around,
Although of course the battle don't alarm me;
And hurrah for the bugle's bray!—
  That's my cue to stay away;
I've taken an objection to the army.

    The lyric of the rest of this song, as printed, was denied by Percy French, and therefore is not being quoted. With fine scorn he drew a line across the other verses of the only copy to hands, and wrote in the margin "re-written by some hack-writer and spoilt! ! P.F."

    It was an early song written in Cavan, in 1890, as a successor to Andy McElroe.

(b) FIGHTING McGUIRE

MAN OF THE NAME OF MAGUIRE

Now, Gibbon has told the story of old,
Of the Fall of the Roman Empire,
But I would recall the rise an' the fall
Of a man of the name of McGuire.
He came to our town as a man of renown
And peace was, he said, his desire,
Still he'd frequently state' what would be the sad fate
Of the man who molested McGuire.

Well, we all were afraid of this quarrelsome blade,
An' we told him to draw near the fire,
An' laughed at his jest, tho' it wasn't the best,
An' swore there's no man like McGuire.
An' when he came up with the neighbours to sup,
His friendliness all would admire,
An' he'd have the best bed—for we'd sleep in the shed
For fear of insulting McGuire.

But MacGilligan's Dan—who's a rale fightin' man,
Said, "Of all this tall talkin' I tire,
I'll step in an' see whyever should he
Be called always Fightin' McGuire.
I'll step in and say, in a casual way,
That I think he's a thief and a liar,
Then I'll hit him a clout, and unless I misdoubt,
That's a way of insulting McGuire."

Then onward he strode to McGuire's abode,
His glorious eye shootin' fire,
An' we thought as he passed we have all looked our last
On the man who insulted McGuire;

Then we listened with grief while we heard him called thief,
An' abused as a rogue an' a liar;
Oh, we all held our breath, for we know it was death
To give any chat to McGuire.

Well, the row wasn't long, but 'twas hot an' 'twas strong
An' the noise it grew higher an' higher
Then it stopt!—an' we said, "Oh begorra, he's dead!
He's been kilt out an' out be McGuire!"
Then out like a thrush from a hawthorn bush
Came something in tattered attire,
And after it fled the man we thought dead—
The man who malthreated McGuire.

'Twas MacGilligan's son, the victory won,
An' we crowded around to admire
The bowld-hearted boy who was first to distroy
The Yoke of the Tyrant McGuire.
An' altho' it's not true, we all said that we knew
From the first he was only a liar,
An' we'd all had a mind to attack—from behind—
That cowardly scoundrel—McGuire.

Although the words were preserved, the tune of "Fighting McGuire"
was lost until quite recently, when it was found in the British Museum.
It is also an early song, dating from 1891.

(c) THE FORTUNES OF FINNEGAN

'Twas Branagan an' Flanagan were talking at the "crass,"
When up comes Larry Lanagan a drivin' of an ass.
Says he "Poor Peter Finnegan is laid out mighty flat—
While readin' his supper he was bitten by the cat."

Chorus.

Says Branagan to Flanagan, an' Flanagan to Lanagan,
"Little Peter Finnegan will not get over that."
But Little Peter Finnegan is runnin' out an' in agin,
For that wan taste of Finnegan had paralysed the cat.

When Peter grew up big an' brown, a blacksmith he was made,
An' not a man in all the town could beat him at his trade.
One day to chase some corner boys he rushed out of his shed,
A motor-car was passin' an' it struck him on the head.

Chorus.

Says Branagan to Flanagan, an' Flanagan to Lanagan,
"I hear that Peter Finnegan has gone to glory clean."
But brawny Peter Finnegan's a horrid man to rin agin—
They found that Peter Finnegan was mendin' the machine.

The boys in all the Barony were courtin' Mary Flynn,
An' no one but that Finnegan would have a chance to win
All the others when they'd meet her 'bout the dowry would begin;
"But I'll take you, girl," says Peter, "In the clothes you're standin' in!"

Chorus.

Says Branagan to Flanagan, an' Flanagan to Lanagan,
"It isn't Peter Finnegan she'll honour an' obey."
But sorra a man but Finnegan will flirt wid Mary Flynn agin,
For bruisin' Peter Finnegan she married yesterday.

'Twas politics that Finnegan would study day an' night;
He'd argue right was mostly wrong an' black was really white.
And when the next election came the posters on the wall
Read, "Vote for Peter Finnegan and the divil a tax at all!"

Chorus.

Says Branagan to Flanagan, an' Flanagan to Lanagan,
"The vote that Peter votes himself his only vote will be."
But Finnegan can win agin, no matter who he's in agin,
And bruisin' Peter Finnegan is Finnegan M.P.

The date of this song is uncertain, but it was written in collaboration
with Collisson, probably for one of the London seasons, after the start
of the new century.

Finnegan was one of these 'tough' Irishmen for whose resilience
W.P.F. had great respect, for he wrote of them several times.

(d) MULLIGAN'S MASQUERADE

Oh! the Mulligans were the champions at The High Society game:
Molly Mulligan's dancing of the Paw-de-Cat
Was an after supper drame;
Their Fate Champate was an illigant trate,
And so we all agrade,
If we got an invitation, we would not be late
At Mulligan's masquerade.

Chorus.

And Geraghty went as a "Gondolier,"
Propelling an ass and cart;
Fogarty filled us all wid fear
As "Napoleon Bonaparte"
The supper was great, all one could ate
On the kitchen dresser laid;
"Kitchen dresser" you say? we said "Boofay"
At Mulligan's masquerade.

Bedalia Crow was "Beautiful Snow"
And it made a curious blend;
O'Hoolighan wasn't invited, so
He came as an "Absent Friend"
That boy of Magee's was "Me*fisht*ofeles,"
But we called a spade a spade,
And not bein' civil, we called him "The Divil"
At Mulligan's masquerade.

And Hennissy came as a "Highwayman"
In the hat that his father wore,
They say that's the way that the father begun,
Amaxsin' his little store.
Miss Fay was seen as a Fairy Queen,
In a gauzy skirt arrayed;
We had to keep her behind the screen
At Mulligan's masquerade.

Miss Foxey Farrell was the "Queen of France"
And the sight I never shall forget,
When Hogan, as Hamlet, begged a dance,
From "Maeryanne Toinette"
Mrs. Regan came as a "Woodland Elf"
I don't know what she weighed,
But her very first prance broke all the delft
At Mulligan's masquerade.

> *Chorus.*
>
> Miss Casey, as "Cycling" took the floor.
> In a corderoys and a kilt;
> Her father patched up the old cuttamore
> And came as a "Crazy Quilt"
> Miss Mullaby as "Joan of Cork"
> Her beautiful shape displayed;
> Faith! many a scarecrow you'd remark
> At Mulligan's masquerade.

The order of the occurrence is not certain, but it might not be too
much off the mark to suggest that it might have come into his head
after his short experience of the Cooney family!

(e) DRUMCOLLIHER

I've been to a great many places,
And wonderful sights I've seen
From Aghernavoe to Ballinasloe
And back to Ballyporeen.
But when they talk of the towns that
Over the ocean lie—
When they say to me, "Pat, what do you think of that?"
I ups and I says, says I—

> *Chorus:*
>
> "I suppose you've not been to Drumcolliher?
> Ye haven't? Well now I declare,
> You must wait till you've been to Drumcolliher
> And see the fine place we have there,
> There's only one street in Drumcolliher,
> But then 'tis a glory to see;
> Ye may talk till you're dumb, but give me ould Drum,
> For Drum is the place for me."

They tell me there's Isles of the Ocean
By India's golden shore,
Where life all day long is a beautiful song,
With flowers and fruits galore;
They tell me the sun does be shining,
With never a cloud in the sky—
But when they have done with their clouds and their sun,
I ups and I says, says I—

Chorus:

"I suppose you've not been to Drumcolliher?
Ye haven't? Well now I declare.
You must wait till you've been to Drumcolliher,
And seen the fine sun we have there,
There's only one sun in Drumcolliher,
And then 'tis a glory to see;
You may talk till you're dumb, but give me ould Drum,
For Drum is the place for me."

I was over in London quite lately,
I gave King Edward a call;
Says the butler, "He's out, he isn't about,
An' I don't see his hat in the hall;
But if you like to look round, sir,
I think you will have to say,
Apartments like these are not what one sees
In your country every day."

Chorus:

Says I, "Have yez been to Drumcolliher?
Ye haven't? Well, now I declare,
You must wait till you've been to Drumcolliher,
And seen the fine house we have there.
There's only one house in Drumcolliher,
For hardware, bacon, and tea;
If your master would come we would treat him in Drum.
Oh! Drum is the place for me."

This number, in swinging waltz time, is one of the better known
songs. It bears a remarkable resemblance to an older ballad called
"Kildorrery" of which the author is unknown, both in tune and words.

Drumcolliher dates from 1900, although it is probable that the verse about King Edward came later—French is fond of references to Edward, and it appears that (as possibly in "The Mountains of Mourne") he changed verses to include these references when he felt the need.

French quite often changed the words of songs in a minor way as use or performance demanded—so that the words of a song as he performed it in later years might differ somewhat from the lyric as first published; this happens with most performers—what he objected to was other people changing his lyrics for him!

(f) KITTY GALLAGHER

Oh, I've courted many a one,
And me heart has been undone,
So often that ye'd think that it was gone o' me;
But faith I know 'tis there
Since I first was made aware
Of beautiful Miss Kitty's physionomy.
Talk of Venus! she was no way her superior
Talk of Lily Langtry! she would sing uncommon small!
Mary Ann McGilligan was every way inferior;
Pretty Kitty Gallagher's the darlin' of them all.

Chorus:

Pretty Kitty Gallagher, sure and I could swallow her,
She'd be cream and sugar in me tay:
Oh! Pretty Kitty Gallagher, faith, and I could follow her,
Over all the world and away.

I fought the whole townland,
And the Finn McCool brass band,
Who thought they had a sort of prior claim to her;
But with me kippeen in me hand,
Faith I made them understand
That Brady was the man to give a name to her.
Mick McCoogan would persuade me to surrender her,
Now he finds it difficult to use a brush and comb,
I dunno if his head or if his heart is now the tenderer
We fought for pretty Kitty till the cows were coming home.

Chorus:

Pretty Kitty Gallagher, sure, etc.

Of no man was I afraid;
But they made an ambuscade;
A course that would have paralysed Napoleon:
But before they laid me out
Faith I caught them many a clout,
You wouldn't find a head but was a holey 'un!
When Miss Kitty seen the broken-headed regiment,
Paradin' out in front of her and askin' her to wife,
Kneelin' down beside me corp the duck of diamonds said she meant
To take the man they murdered and that brought me back to life!

Chorus:

Pretty Kitty Gallagher, sure, etc.

Another charming song. In Percy French's litany of love affairs in
song the prize goes to the assured and direct lovers of "Eileen Oge" and
"The Girl from Clare"—which is usually the way in life: but Kitty
Gallagher picks the man who gets knocked out for her sake, and
good luck to her!

(g) "TULLINAHAW"

It was Sergeant Kilray of the Cavan Police
    Was heard for to say "Crime's on the increase
And the worst of the lot for breakin' the law
    Were the boys that you've got in Tullinahaw.
Cattle they're drivin,' drivin', tarrable,
    Wantin' the whole of Ireland arable,
Meescheef that soon'd be irreparable
    If it's not squinch'd in Tullinahaw".
So Sergeant Kilray an' Constable Flynn
    Started away that night to begin
Bringin' a taste of ordher an' law
    For man an' for baste in Tullinahaw.

Oh they lay by the wall an' they kep' wide awake
   Till they saw a man haulin' a cow to the lake.
"Honest man, tell me now is that cow all your own?"
   "Is it me own a cow that's all skin and bone?
Sure she belongs to Widda Geraghty
   Home I was drivin' her from charity."
"Tell me", says Flynn—with some hilarity,
   "Why are you comin' from Tullinahaw?"
An' Sergeant Kilray was heard for to say
   "The case is suspeecious in ev-er-y way"
And Flynn said he saw a breach of the law
   In drivin' a cow from Tullinahaw.

Oh the trial came on an' the prisoner swore
   He was doin' a neighbourly act an' no more,
For the cow was no use and the Widda that day
   Had give him a bob to take it away!
"Stop!" said the Judge, "You've made no case of it
   That is a lie, sir, on the face of it,
Perjury too there's ev'ry trace of it,
   Years they'll miss you in Tullinahaw".
And Sergeant Kilray and Constable Flynn,
   They made no delay in runnin' him in.
An' there for a year he sits in the straw
   Lamentin' the grandeurs of Tullinahaw.

When they brought back the cow, says the Widda "Ochone!
   How I wish them police would leave people alone,
For if I could have proved the ould reptile was drown'd
   I'd ha' got compinsation—aye—nine or ten pound.
Instid of the money to help further me,
   Here the ould baste is back to bother me,
Whin John comes out I know he'll murther me,
   Gettin' him took in Tullinahaw".
An' Sergeant Kilray and Constable Flynn,
   The both of them grey and elderly min,
Still tell how they brought back ordher an' law—
   'Tis a different story in Tullinahaw!

This breezy song was probably written around 1910, or possibly a
little later.
   It is one of the better neglected numbers.

(*h*) AN IRISH MOTHER

A wee slip drawin' water,
    Me ould man at the plough,
No grown-up son nor daughter,
    That's the way we're farmin' now.
"No work and little pleasure"
    Was the cry before they wint,
Now they're gettin' both full measure,
    So I ought to be contint.

Great wages men is givin'
    In that land beyant the say,
But 'tis lonely-lonely livin'
    Whin the childher is away.

Och, the baby in the cradle,
    Blue eyes and curlin' hair,
God knows I'd give a gra'dle
    To have little Pether there;
No doubt he'd find it funny
    Lyin' here upon me arm,
Him—that's earnin' the good money,
    On a Californy farm.

Six pounds it was or sivin
    He sint last quarter day,
But 'tis lonely-lonely livin'
    Whin the childher is away.

God is good—no better,
    And the Divil might be worse,
Each month there comes a letther
    Bringing somethin' for the purse.
And me ould man's heart rejoices
    Whin I read they're doin' fine,
But it's oh! to hear their voices,
    And to feel their hands in mine.

To see the cattle drivin'
    And the young ones makin' hay,
"Tis a lonely land to live in
    Whin the childher is away."

Whin the shadders do be fallin'
    On the ould man there an' me,
'Tis hard to keep from callin'
    "Come in, childher, to yer tea!"
I can almost hear them comin'
    Mary Kate and little Con,—
Och! but I'm a foolish woman,
    Sure they're all grown up an' gone.

That our sins may be forgiven,
    And not wan go asthray,
I doubt I'd stay in Heaven
    If them childher was away.

This was a poem without music until quite recently when Brendan O'Dowda wrote a tune for it. If anybody thinks Percy French didn't understand the feelings of an Irish mother perhaps they might read this song.

APPENDIX II

SONG CYCLES AND COMIC OPERAS

(*a*) A Kerry Courting, Song Cycle—Complete Words.

(*b*) The Knight of the Road, or The Irish Girl

SELECTED LYRICS WITH NOTES

Street Ballad.
Hunting Song.
Irish Jaunting Car, The
Oft in my Dreaming
Highwayman, The
Girl on the Big Black Mare, The

(*c*) Freda and the Fairies

SELECTED LYRICS WITH NOTES

A Fairy Song
Who said the Hook never hurted the worm?
I've fought a fierce Hyena.

(*d*) "Noah's Ark" was not published, but two of the songs (The Hoodoo, and Pretendy Land), which are included in the text, were published separately.

(*e*) "Strongbow" was not published and the lyrics have been lost.

A KERRY COURTING

IRISH SONG-CYCLE

by

PERCY FRENCH AND HOUSTON COLLISSON

CHARACTERS

MARY CAREY (The Rose of Tralee)	*Contralto*
MRS. CAREY (Her Mother)	*Soprano*
YOUNG MAGEE (In Love with Mary)	*Tenor*
OLD MAGEE (His Father)	*Baritone or Bass*

MRS. CAREY—

    Oh Mary, it's time ye were married,
      I don't say yer much of a catch,
    Wid never a pound in the bank I'll be bound
      No boy will be liftin' the latch.

    But boys are mysterious creatures,
      And when one is crazy to wed,
        A girl might bring
        Him to buy her the ring
    Before he got right in his head.

    And they call ye "The Rose o' Tralee,"
                      Dear me,
        It's all very pretty to be
        A beautiful rose,
        But Lord only knows
    Who'll marry "The Rose o' Tralee,"
                      D'ye see?
    Who'll marry "The Rose o' Tralee?"

    Still Janey Delaney got married,
      Although she looks two ways at wance;
    And Carroty Peg with the twist in her leg.
      So I'm thinkin' ye might have a chance.

    Of course those two fairies had money
      That gave them a bit of a push,
        But all that you've got
        In the crockery pot
    Wouldn't whistle a boy off the bush.

And they call ye "The Rose o' Tralee,"
>   Dear me,
> It's all very pretty to be
>   A beautiful rose,
>   But the Lord only knows
> Who'll marry "The Rose o' Tralee,"
>   D'ye see?
> Who'll marry "The Rose o' Tralee?"

MARY—

> Oh mother dear, give over,
> Sure I'm living here in clover,
> And I'm sure there's not a rover
>   That would care to marry me:
>
> And there isn't any party
> That I'd take to very hearty,
> Unless 'twas Dan McCarthy,
>   Or young Joyce—or Pat Magee.
>
> Oh there's his father knockin',
> 'Tis himself that will be mockin',
> For there's nothing in the stockin'
>   That will make him fond o' me.
>
> But 'tis little use to snivel,
> Just be sensible and civil,
> Tell the truth and shame the divil,
>   For my heart's with Pag Magee.

> *(Enter the Magees, father and son).*

OLD MAGEE—

> "God save all here!"
> How are ye, Mrs. Carey?

MRS. CAREY—

> God save you, sir!

OLD MAGEE—

> Good evenin' to ye, Mary.
> *(Sits by Mary, young Pat sits by Mrs. Carey).*

MRS. CAREY—

>Yer axin' how am I? Oh now, middlin' well,
>>D'ye mind the cow that I wanted to sell?
>The sorra a drop o' milk will she give,
>>O it's terrible hard for a widda to live.

>If it wasn't for Mary I'd soon be destroyed,
>>An' it's only the truth to be told,
>She's worth any two men that ye ever employed,
>>She's worth forty years' purchase in gold.

OLD MAGEE—

>I might say the same of young Pat, so I might,
>>Contrivin' and workin, from mornin' till night,
>He's on for a wife, but of course he allows
>>She should bring forty pounds or a couple of cows.

MRS. CAREY—

>Forty pounds did ye say? and me last penny spent
>>On the lawyers that settled me judical rent;
>I'll give her me blessin' and give her ten pounds,
>>And if that's not enough just be off on yer rounds!

ENSEMBLE—

>Oh, it's very aisy talkin'
>>But to me it's very clear
>Ye }
>We } had better both be walkin'
>>For ye }
>>we } arn't wanted here.
>There's plenty ye }
>>we } can pick,—
>Let 'em }
>us } go, let 'em }
>us } go.
>Take up the hat and stick,
>>And be marchin' mighty quick
>There's a little widda waitin'
>>Down below.

YOUNG PAT—

    I'd like to say a word to you
        Before we try next door,
    I've saved about enough for two,
        Perhaps a trifle more;
    If Mary has no money
        I wouldn't care a pin,
    For I'd marry you, me honey,
        In the clothes yer standing in!
    (*Goes and stands behind Mary*).
    I've worked as hard as any man
        For more than seven year,
    And all the while I had a plan
        I'll whisper in yer ear.
    If she hasn't got a shilling
        I'll be glad as one can be,
    For if Mary Carey's willing,
        She's the girl for Pat Magee.

OLD MAGEE—

    You might have had a cow you fool,
        As aisy as the day.

MRS. CAREY—

    Sit down, ould Pat, sit down me jool,
        Now what does Mary say?

MARY—

    I've heard a many pleasant songs,
        And thought them sweet to hear,
    But ne'er a wan did ever sound
        So sweetly in my ear.
    "If the girl has got no money
        I wouldn't care a pin,
    For I'll marry you, me honey,
        In the clothes yer standin' in."

    And mother wouldn't let me go
        Without me twenty pound,
    She told me that she had it, so
        You'll get it, I'll be bound.

A stockin' she's been filling,
    For the boy who comes for me,
And the girl is more than willing
    If the boy is Pat Magee.

OLD MAGEE—

You might have had the cow, me lad.

MRS. CAREY—

You might have had the moon.

YOUNG PAT—

I've got the moon and stars bedad.

MARY—

And I've the sun aroon.

Solo

OLD MAGEE—

    Ah! then, Mary,
    Arn't ye contrary,
To be talking to the boy like that.
    Well ye know
    A cow or so
Is nothing for a boy like Pat.
    He may think ye
    Worth a lot of money
Till the favour of his love's gone by.
    Then "My sowl!
    What an owl
Them two Carey women made o' me."
    And that will be the boyo's cry.

MRS. CAREY—

Now I think it's just as well if I
    Boiled the kettle and wet the tay,
Whisky, too, our throats 'id millify,
    After all you've had to say.
Take the cake from off the griddle an'
    Soon ye'll have yer bite and sup;
Hand ould Pat the bow and fiddle an'
    Don't be long in jiggin' it up!

PAT MAGEE—

    Here's to the nest, and it's me that'll feather it
    I'll make it the finest that ever you see!
    Here's to the Rose!

OLD MAGEE—

    And the boy that'll gather it,
    Here's Mary Carey "The Rose of Tralee!"

(*b*) "THE KNIGHT OF THE ROAD"

(*later known as* "*The Irish Girl*")

COMEDY OPERA IN THREE ACTS

Book and lyrics by Percy French (assisted by Brendan Stewart)

Music by Houston Collisson

ACT I.—The Hiring Fair at the Village of Boneenbeg, Co. Galway.
    (*Exterior of the* "*O'Hara Arms*" *Inn*)

ACT II.—The Mountain Pass on the way to the Ball (*midnight*).

ACT III.—The Tenants' Ball at Castle Desmond (*Vestibule of the Ballroom*).

Time: The unsettled time in Ireland, following the rising of 1798.

"The Knight of the Road" tells of the exploits of Jack Freeny, who was a real life Robin Hood character in Ireland at the start of the nineteenth century, and is based on a section of an old book called "Irish Rogues and Raparees".

A Highland Regiment, led by a Captain Anstruther are out after the highwayman and come to the "O'Hara Arms" on their way. Fegan, the landlord, is expecting Freeny that day, but, like most of the people, is in sympathy with the outlaw, and when he arrives disguised as a ballad singer helps him to escape. In this he is aided by Kathleen O'Hara, an heiress who has arrived at the Inn with a hunting party, and also owes Freeny a debt of gratitude.

Despite their difference over Freeny Anstruther falls for Miss O'Hara. Sir George Desmond, master of the Hunt, is giving a tenants' ball at Castle Desmond, and on the way to it, Miss O'Hara, travelling with her uncle, the impecunious Sir Henry Lefanu, again encounters Freeny when he holds up the coach. He is again caught by Anstruther and his men, who have been lying in ambush. Freeny is left in charge of Paddy Flynn a comic Irish soldier who had enlisted in the Highlanders, and once more escapes, driving off in the coach, after exchanging clothes with an unwilling Sir Henry. At the ball there is some confusion since, due to the mishaps on the way, several people turn up in the wrong clothes, but eventually Freeny arrives and discloses that he has found a pardon in the pocket of the coat which he had "borrowed" from Sir Henry, so that all ends happily in the end.

The plot "staggers" a bit in the last act, but there is plenty of interest in the show right through, and as it has quite a lot of lively comedy, it would be interesting to see how this musical play would do in a revival. It could be quite successful.

Much of the "by-play" comes from Paddy Flynn, the reluctant soldier-boy (one of a kin with Cornelius Burke, Andy McElroe and others of the songs) and his affair with Mary, daughter of the innkeeper, is edged by the attendance of the Scots soldier McKinnon.

There are several interesting lyrics. In one, Freeny and his companion Peg pose as street singers on their first entry.

STREET BALLAD

COME ALL YE FINE LADIES

Come, all ye fine ladies and gentlemen, too,
Attend to me singin' and I'll tell ye true
About a brave boy who lived out in the cold,
And the name that he went by was "Freeny the Bold."
    Tur-in-ah, tur-in-ah, tur-in-an-the-dan-day.

Now Jack was a robber upon the highway,
And stopped the mail-coaches be night and be day;
What he took from the rich he would give to the poor,
So of Poverty's blessin' he always was sure.
    Tur-in-ah, tur-in-ah, tur-in-an-the-dan-day.

One day when the coach had set off for the fair,
It was met be Jack Freeny bestridin' his mare:
Some called for the soldiers, some called for the watch
And one lady called for two-penn' worth of Scotch.
    Tur-in-ah, tur-in-ah, tur-in-an-the-dan-day.

The guard held his blunderbuss out on full cock,
Sez he, "Jack, clear out, or you'll know what's o'clock."
Jack flattened him out wid the butt of his gun,
Sez he, "What's o'clock? Well, it's just strikin' one."
    Tur-in-ah, tur-in-ah, tur-in-an-the-dan-day.

So the gentlemen pulled out their purses of gold,
And handed them over to Freeny the Bold:
Sez Freeny, "Me boys, ye got off mighty well,
I'd ha' fleeced ye far more if I'd kept an hotel."
    Tur-in-ah, tur-in-ah, tur-in-an-the-dan-day.

Now, all ye fine ladies and gintlemen, too,
Ye've heard from my singin'—and I've told ye true,
All about the brave boy who lived out in the cold,
And the name that he went be was "Freeny the Bold."
    Tur-in-ah, tur-in-ah, tur-in-an-the-dan-day.

There is a genuine old ballad called "Bold Captain Freney" which
French may have been familiar with. The real Freney operated in
Kilkenny, not in Galway, and died a respectable "lock-keeper" in
New Ross.

Some of the lyrics are in a conventional strain, as for instance the
Hunting Song, which nevertheless echoes French the countryman.

HUNTING SONG AND CHORUS

Oh, what is so delightful on a bright December morn
                As the ringing echoes flinging
                From the hunter's horn!
And sailing o'er the upland at the dawning of the day.
                Follow! Follow! the view hallo!
                For'ard, hark, away!

        The fox is gone, the hounds are on,
                Away we fly,
        O'er hill and dale, o'er post and rail,
                O'er fences high.
        The man from town would cut us down,
                But soon they find
        That we can stay as well as they,
                And leave them far behind

Chorus:

Oh, what is so delightful, etc.

        Then the returning as the sun goes down,
        Over the fallow and the heather brown,
        Telling the story of the run again;
        Dreaming, we listen to the glad refrain.

Chorus:

        Tally ho! Tally ho! Tally ho!
        She's our toast sir, Galway's boast, sir,
        Who refuses, pistols chooses.
        Oh! but she's a handsome creature,
        Fairy-like in form and feature,
        Not a man of them can teach her.

Chorus:

Oh, what is so delightful, etc.

One which gallops along in fine style, reminiscent a little of Lover's
"Low-backed car" is the duet between Anstruther and Kathleen
"An Irish Jaunting Car".

THE IRISH JAUNTING CAR

Some say that to float
Down a stream in a boat
    Will bring any man to your feet:
And some people talk
Of a moonlight walk
    As an equally certain receipt.
But better than dreaming on silvery stream,
    And better than moonlight or star,
Is just to contrive to go for a drive
    On an Irish jaunting car.

Oh! the Irish jaunting car!
From Bantry to Ballingar—
    You always begin
    By tucking her in
On the side of the jaunting car,
    Of an Irish jaunting car.
    If fond of the girl you are,
    It takes a good while
    To fix her in style
On the side of the jaunting car.

When you fly round a turn
One thing you must learn
    That really you ought to know,
Put your arm round and grip
Her, for fear she should slip—
    And don't be too quick letting go.
For when your arm's placed
Round her elegant waist
    There might come a terrible jolt—
If your arm wasn't there,
She'd be kill'd, I declare,
So there's reason for holding your bolt.

Oh! the Irish jaunting car!
When it comes to a jolt or a jar,
　　You have every right
　　To be holding her tight
On the Irish jaunting car.
　　When out on an outside car
　　The weather is really no bar,
　　If it comes on to rain
　　You never complain
On the Irish jaunting car.

There's a flush on her cheek,
And you venture to speak
　　Of making her some day your own:
Her eyes are quite kind,
But she begs to remind
　　You that "really, we are not alone."
Oh, the driver is blind,
And the horse doesn't mind
　　If you're going a bit too far,
And the crack of the whip
Covers lip meeting lip
　　On the back of the jaunting car.

Oh! the Irish jaunting car!
Your fortune 'twill make or mar:
　　For you've woo'd and you've won
　　Before you have done
On the Irish jaunting car.
　　On the Irish jaunting car
　　You may trust she's your lucky star,
　　For Cupid has set
　　His cunningest net
On an Irish jaunting car.

Peg, the wild child of the countryside, who fears that Freeny's
wanderings will only end on the hangman's rope has several lyrics
which are reminiscent of "Gortnamona", particularly this one from
the first act.

OFT IN MY DREAMING

Oft in my dreaming
 Those bright eyes I see,
And in their beaming
 They beam, they beam on me!
When I awaken
 The daylight seems so drear,
I am forsaken,
 For then you are not near.

When twilight falling
 Has dimmed the distant view,
My heart, my heart is calling,
 Calling, my love, to you!
'Twas but a fleeting vision,
 And yet when dies the day,
It comes, that dream Elysian,
 That will not fade away!

Come in my dreaming,
 And some day, oh, my sweet,
In all your beauty beaming,
 Once more we two may meet.
Heart! heart! love laden,
 Ah, tell me when 'twill be—
I know it is the maiden
 That Fate has found for me.

Freeny's song of how he became a highwayman has a Gilbertian ring.

THE HIGHWAYMAN

When I was a child I was meek and mild
 And quite as good as gold;
I was, in fact, in word and act
 A pattern to behold.
My father would stand with a stick in his hand
 My morning hymn to hear,
If I missed a line he would fan my spine,
 While mother enlarged my ear.

Chorus:

They brought me up on the strictest plan—
That's why I became a highwayman.

Oh, Sunday was gay, all my toys put away
    And a book put in my hand,
Called "Faith and Work" by Ignatius Burke,
    Which I never could understand.
Then Tommy McGee would whisper to me,
    "Let's go off and fish for perch."
I'd have loved to go but I answered "No,"
    As I passed on my way to church.

Chorus:

Then as a rule my life at school
    I couldn't quite enjoy
For I was licked by the boys and kicked
    For being a model boy.
On the least pretex' I'd have wrung their necks,
    I was strong for a boy of my size;
But I knew I'd be whaled by my dad if I failed
    To bring home the good conduct prize.

Chorus:

I got so good, men said I would
    Be dead before my prime,
So my parents thought they really ought
    To choose my profession in time.
I was going to say that I'd like some day
    To run away to sea,
Or else enlist, but my father said, "Whisht,
    He was made for the Ministree."

Chorus.

Lastly when Anstruther sings of the girl he would marry we come to a number which, musically, is a gem.

THE GIRL ON A BIG BLACK MARE

The Girl that I had in my mind

The girl that I had in my mind, the one that I could love,
　　Was rather tall and stately, with a queen-like air;
How often have my fingers twined around her perfumed glove,
　　As in dreams she gently murmured, "You may not despair!"
But this lady has been banished to "the deuce knows where,"
By a West-of-Shannon beauty on a big black mare.

I dreamt of floating idly on a gentle flowing stream,
　　A siren seated by me with her golden hair,
Who sang to me sweet melodies that echoed through my dream,
　　And while the vision lasted all the earth was fair.
But now my nightly vision and my daily care
Is the girl who nearly brained me with her big black mare.

(c) "FREDA AND THE FAIRIES"

OPERETTA IN TWO ACTS FOR CHILDREN

Libretto by Percy French
Lyrics by Percy French and Cicely Fox-Smith
Music by Caroline Maude (Viscountess Hawarden)

"Freda" is a pleasant little piece, with a cast of nine principals, and
chorus. Three of the parts are really speaking chorus parts. It is ideally

suitable for a girls' school, with small girls playing the gnomes and fairies, and slightly bigger ones taking the parts of Freda ("a good little girl of ten") and Sammy ("a bad little boy of twelve").

Alternatively, it is even more suitable for the junior grades of a mixed school.

Mab, the Queen of the Fairies, is upset because while the fairies were off dancing the gnomes have rented a burrow near them from a mole, and are disturbing the fairies with the sound of their hammers. The fairies return from their revels.

A FAIRY SONG

Stay, silver ray,
Till our airy way we wing
To the shade of the glade
Where the fairies dance and sing:
The mortals are asleep—
They can never understand
That night brings delight,
It is day in Fairyland.

Float, golden note,
From the lute strings all in tune,
Climb, quiv'ring chime,
Up the moonbeams to the moon.
There is music on the river,
There is music on the strand
Night brings delight,
It is day in Fairyland.

Sing while we swing
From the bluebell's lofty crest.
"Hey! Come and play,
Sleepy songbirds in your nest;
The glow-worm lamps are lit,
Come and join our elfin band,
Night brings delight,
It is day in Fairyland."

Roam thro' the home
Where the little children sleep,
Light in our flight
Where the curly ringlets peep.
Some shining eyes may see us,
But the babies understand,
Night brings delight,
It is day in Fairyland.

The Queen learns from the other fairies that a little girl has fallen
asleep in a fairy ring and will, therefore, have to do their bidding for
a year: she conceives the idea that this girl, Freda, could be used to
drive out the little gnomes.

The gnomes, led by their King, Blum, and his short-sighted secretary,
Kobbee, face the fairies, and are not too happy at the thought of war,
but are more sanguine when they find a little boy stuck in their chimney
whom they adopt as *their* champion.

He is Sammy, known as a terror to all the animals of the district.
The King and Kobbee remind him of his petty cruelties.

WHO SAID THE HOOK NEVER HURTED THE WORMS?

Who said the hook never hurted the worms?
Who only laughed at their struggles and squirms?
Who? who?
Who left the minnows to die on the bank?
Who grinned a grin when the last kitten sank?
Who? who?
From sun shiny plain and from caverns cool,
The ghosts of the slain echo,
"Sammy skip-school."

Who shot the pigeon they baked in a pie?
Who pulled the wings off a poor little fly?
Who? who?
Who chased and frightened a poor little lamb?
Who broke the window, and who stole the jam?
Who? who?
From sun shiny plain and from caverns cool,
The ghosts of the slain echo,
"Sammy skip-school."

The gnomes dress Sammy in shining armour and set him to face Freda. The two children taunt each other in a boastful way, very reminiscent of a number in a musical show written many years later—"Anything you can do I can do better" from "Annie get your Gun".

THE BOASTING OF SAMMY AND FREDA

SAMMY: I've fought a fierce hyena,
He was just as high as high!

FREDA: So have I, so have I!
Mine was higher than the sky.

CHORUS: Only fancy killing something that was higher than the sky.

SAMMY: I have killed a hipperpotomus,
Much bigger than a wall,

FREDA: Is that all? that was small,
Mine was nearly twice as tall.

CHORUS: Just fancy killing something that was nearly twice as tall.

BOTH: I know you don't believe me,
That is plain enough to see,
But once I killed a beetle,
And I've often killed a bee.

SAMMY: I killed a dreadful dragon
That drank up the Forth of Firth.

FREDA: So did mine, so did mine!
He just swallowed up the earth.

CHORUS: Only fancy killing something that could swallow up the earth.

SAMMY: I have killed a great sea-serpent,
Yes I killed it with an axe.

FREDA: I killed six, with some bricks
And a bit of cobbler's wax.

CHORUS: How clever to kill serpents with a bit of cobbler's wax.

BOTH: I know you don't believe me, etc.

SAMMY: I only use a pop-gun
          When I kill a tiger-cat.

FREDA: I killed mine with some twine—
          Just about as long as that.

CHORUS: Killing tiger-cats with pop-guns and a string as long as that.

SAMMY: I was fishing off an ice-berg,
          And I caught a 'normous whale.

FREDA: I caught five, all alive,
          And I keep them in a pail.

CHORUS: How wonderful to keep 'normous fishes in a pail.

BOTH: I know you don't believe me, etc.

Freda throws the helmet up and finds it is only Sammy after all. They declare the "war" is over, and the gnomes march off, leaving the fairies at peace. A simple and charming musical miniature. Four of the twenty lyrics are by Cicely Fox-Smith, and the remainder by Percy French. All those quoted are by Percy French.

APPENDIX III

COMPLETE LIST OF SONGS AND OTHER MUSICAL WORKS

	Page	Year written	Music published by	Composed or arranged by
Abdulla Bulbul Ameer	5	1877	Ascherberg, Hopwood, and Crewe, Ltd.	Percy French
Ach, I dunno	97	—	Keith Prowse Music Publishing Co. Ltd. by arrangement with Pigott & Co.	Molly H. French (1957)
All by the Baltic Say.	111	1914	Pigott & Co.	arr. L. Braid on old ballad.
Am Tag	109	1914	Pigott & Co.	Percy French and L. Braid.
Andy McElroe	26	1888	Pigott & Co.	with J. Ross.
Are ye right there Michael?	50	1902	Keith Prowse Music Publishing Co. Ltd.	Percy French
Bad Ballads for Baddish Babies. (Song Cyclette)	86	1910	Ascherberg, Hopwood, and Crewe, Ltd.	Houston Collisson
Ballymilligan	127	—	Keith Prowse Music Publishing Co. Ltd.	arr. Molly French (1952) on tune "The Fisherman's Lament"

	Page	Year written	Music published by	Composed or arranged by
Come-all-ye	113	—	Keith Prowse Music Publishing Co. Ltd. (1963)	Parody of old ballad— Percy French.
Come Back, Paddy Reilly to Ballyjamesduff.	24	1912	Keith Prowse Music Publishing Co. by arrangement with Pigott & Co.	Percy French.
Cornelius Burke	132	1890	Francis Day & Hunter (Now reverted to French family)	Percy French.
Darlin' girl from Clare.	54	1906	Pigott & Co.	Percy French.
Darlin' girl from Clare (ladies' version)	56	after 1906	Not published	Percy French.
Donegan's Daughter.	81	before or during 1906	Joseph Williams Ltd.	W. H. Collisson.
Drumcolliher	137	1900	Keith Prowse Music Publishing Co. Ltd.	Percy French.
Eileen Oge	37	1903	Keith Prowse Music Publishing Co. Ltd.	arr. Houston Collisson.
Emigrant's Letter, The	89	1910	Keith Prowse Music Publishing Co. Ltd.	Ernest Hastings.

	Page	Year written	Music published by	Composed or arranged by
Emigrant Ship, The	91	1890	Pigott & Co.	Percy French.
Father O'Callaghan.	71	c.1906	Ascherberg, Hopwood, and Crewe, Ltd.	Houston Collisson.
Fighting McGuire	133	1891	Keith Prowse Music Publishing Co. Ltd.	Percy French.
Flaherty's Drake	116	—	Keith Prowse Music Publishing Co. Ltd. (1963)	Percy French on Trad. tune
Flanagan's Flying Machine.	106	1911	Pigott & Co.	W. H. Collisson.
Fortunes of Finnegan.	134	c.1900	Pigott & Co.	W. H. Collisson.
From Freda and the Fairies.	158	—	Novello & Co.	Caroline Maude (Viscountess Hawarden) some lyrics by Cicely Fox-Smith.
Gortnamona	32	—	Keith Prowse Music Publishing Co. Ltd.	Philip Green (1958)
Hoodoo, The (from "Noah's Ark")	20	1907	Ascherberg, Hopwood and Crewe, Ltd. (1910)	Houston Collisson.

	Page	Year written	Music published by	Composed or arranged by
Innismeela ...	103	—	Keith Prowse Music Publishing Co. Ltd.	Philip Green (1962) Originally sung to tune by Percy French now lost.
Irish Mother, An	142	—	Keith Prowse Music Publishing Co. Ltd.	Brendan O'Dowda (1962)
Jim Wheelahan's Automobeel.	104	1903	Pigott & Co.	Houston Collisson.
Kerry Courting, The, (Song Cycle)	145	1909	Boosey & Co.	Percy French.
Killyran Wrackers, The	101	pre-1914	Not Published	Percy French.
King Edward in Erin.	75	1907	Weekes & Co.	Houston Collisson.
Kitty Gallagher	139	—	Keith Prowse Music Publishing Co. Ltd.	Percy French.
Knight of the Road, The	150–158	1891	Boosey & Co.	Houston Collisson.
Larry Mick McGarry	119	1915	Keith Prowse Music Publishing Co. Ltd.	Percy French.
Little Brigid Flynn	92	—	Keith Prowse Music Publishing Co. Ltd.	arr. Molly Percy French
Luke the Looney	99	1914	Not Published	Part tune and words lost.

	Page	Year written	Music published by	Composed or arranged by
McBreen's Heifer	77	1900	Keith Prowse Music Publishing Co. Ltd.	arr. and part comp. Percy French.
Maguire's Motor Bike	39	1906	Joseph Williams Ltd.	Houston Collisson
Mary Ann McHugh, The	114	—	Keith Prowse Music Publishing Co. Ltd.	Percy French (based on the old tune "Limerick is Beautiful" Take-off of "The Cruise of Calabar") Re-arranged Phil Green 1962, with new tune.
Mat Hannigan's Aunt.	33	1892	Keith Prowse Music Publishing Co. Ltd.	Percy French.
Mick's Hotel	47	—	Keith Prowse Music Publishing Co. Ltd.	Percy French.
Mountains of Mourne, The	65	1896	Keith Prowse Music Publishing Co. Ltd.	arr. Houston Collisson of traditional tune.
Mulligan's Masquerade.	136	1900	Pigott and Co.	Percy French.
Mrs. Brady	83	1907	Joseph Williams Ltd.	Houston Collisson.

	Page	Year written	Music published by	Composed or arranged by
Next Landing of the French, The	118	—	Not Published	Trad. tune ("Shan Van Vocht"— —Sean bhean bhocht).
Night Miss Cooney Eloped, The	45	apr. 1900	Keith Prowse Music Publishing Co. Ltd.	Percy French.
No more o' yer Golfin' for me	122	1906	Joseph Williams Ltd.	Houston Collisson.
Noah's Ark (Christmas Fairy Musical Play)	20 and 124	c.1907	Not Published	Houston Collisson and J. A. Robertson.
Oklahoma Rose, The	93	1910	Keith Prowse Music Publishing Co. Ltd.	Percy French.
On the Road to Ballybay	128	—	Keith Prowse Music Publishing Co. Ltd.	Molly French on Trad. tune (1938).
Phil the Fluter's Ball	22	1889	Keith Prowse Music Publishing Co. Ltd.	Percy French.
Phistlin' Phil McHugh	60	1901	Keith Prowse Music Publishing Co. Ltd.	Percy French.
Pretendy Land	124	1907	Joseph Williams Ltd. (1915)	J. A. Robertson.

	Page	Year written	Music published by	Composed or arranged by
Rafferty's Racin' Mare	13	1906	Joseph Williams Ltd.	Houston Collisson.
Rafting down the Rio	99	after 1910	Not Published	Tune Lost.
Sailor courted a farmer's daughter	113	*see "Come-all-ye"*		
Shlathery's Mounted Fut	28	1889	Keith Prowse Music Publishing Co. Ltd.	Percy French.
Soldiers Three	35	1892	Pigott & Co.	Percy French.
Sweet Marie	12	after 1910	Not Published	Parody of Traditional American tune
Song of William, Inspector of Drains	16	1881/2	Not Published	Eric Rogers (1961) for "The Golden Years".
Strongbow (opera)	—	1889	Not Published	Houston Collisson.
That's why we're Burying him	94	1912	Francis, Day & Hunter Ltd.	E. G. French (Ettie French)
Tullinahaw	140	—	Ascherberg, Hopwood and Crewe	Trad. arr. Houston Collisson.
Wait for a while now, Mary	69	1906 or before	Joseph Williams Ltd.	Trad. arr. Houston Collisson.
When Erin Wakes	74	1900	Weekes & Co.	Trad. arr. Houston Collisson.

APPENDIX IV

LIST OF OTHER KNOWN WORKS

Poems and Lyrics by Percy French for which no music was written, or for which the music cannot be traced.

Ballinaddy
Carmody's mare
Celestial Paintings
Comic Advertisement
Cremorne
Cruise of the Pirate Bus, The
End of the Holiday, The
Excelsior
Fisherman's Wife, The
Fitzwilliam Square
Four Farrellys, The
Galloping Hogan
George Grossmith
Goosey, Goosey, Gander
Hiawatha's Motoring
How Hiawatha won the cup
If I was a Lady
In exile
In the studio
Islands of Aran
Kindly Welcome, The
Later On
L'Envoi
Lines in a Swiss Hotel
Lines written in praise of Joan Phyllis French.

Little Girl's Prayer, A
Mother's Fairies.
Musician to his Love, The
Not Lost but gone before
Nursery Rhymes, The
Off to the West Indies
Only way out of it, The
Otter King, The
Painter and the Pianist, The
Paradise
People I don't want to meet
Queen's advice to Lord Zetland
Queen's after-dinner speech
"Reaction, A"
Red letter Days
Retrospection
Roley, Poley
Smiles
Sweet Lavender
Tell me, O Captain
Tennis Tournament, The
Things that matter
To E.R.
To the West
Valley of Dunloe, The

Many of these lyrics will be found in Poems, Prose and Parodies of Percy French, published by the Talbot Press, Dublin.

Sketches (S)   Monologues (M)   and "Lectures" (L)

*Children's Party, The
    or the Lion who wouldn't eat Parsley ...   ...   (M)

 Doomed to the Dustbin   ...   .   (M)

*First Lord Lieutenant, The   ...   .   (M)

*Gloom   ...   .   (S)

*Larksmead School breaks up ...   .   (M)

 Lassie, the Loon and the Fighting Dog   ...   ...   (M)

*Letter from the Front, The   ...   .   (S)

*Michael O'Regan gets the pension   ...   .   (S)

 My friend, Magistrate Finnegan   ...   .   (S)

 Napoleon I
    (Why Napoleon Failed to set Fire to the Thames)   (L)

*Examination for the post of Editor of *Irish Cyclist* ...   (M)

 Oldest Joke in the world, The ...   .   (M)

 Our betters the beasts ...   .   (S)

 Our Debating Society ...   .   (S)

 Prehistoric Origin of Man, The   ...   .   (L)

 Some adventures in the Life of Peter Binks ...   ...   (S)

 Story of the Silhouette, The   ...   .   (S)

(This list does not pretend to be complete, and many of these items have not survived. They may, however, be remembered by some of the older generation who heard Mr. French. Items marked * will be found in *Prose, Poems and Parodies*)

APPENDIX V

Bibliography

Chronicles and Poems { edited Mrs. de Burgh Daly
with introduction by Percy French

Prose, Poems and Parodies of Percy French { edited Mrs. de Burgh Daly
Foreword by Alfred Perceval.
Graves, Talbot Press, Dublin.

Percy French by R. B. D. French. (Trinity Magazine, Michaelmas 1954)

Percy French by Val Vousden   (Irish Capuchin Annual 1955)

Dr. Collisson in and on Ireland—W. A. Houston Collisson (Robt. Sutton. London, 1908)

"James O'Mara—A staunch Sinn Feiner"—Patricia Lavelle.

The Stephenson Locomotive Society—No 433. June 1962. (Percy French and the West Clare Railway by Walter McGrath)

OTHER WORKS ON PERCY FRENCH

The Last Troubadour—Radio Biography by Donal Giltenan.

The Golden Years { Musical Play by Donal Giltenan
Music by Percy French and Eric Rogers.

Songs of Percy French—Volumes 1, 2, and 3 (Keith Prowse Music Publishing Co. Ltd.)